Lab Manual

to Accompany

Fundamentals of Electronics: AC Circuits
Volume II

Ernest Arney

ITT Technical Institute

THOMSON
TM
DELMAR LEARNING

Albany • Bonn • Boston • Cincinnati • Detroit • London • Madrid • Melbourne
Mexico City • New York • Pacific Grove • Paris • San Francisco • Singapore
Tokyo • Toronto • Washington

Fundamentals of Electronics
Laboratory Manual Volume 2: AC Circuits

Publisher
Alar Elken

Acquisitions Editor
Gregory Clayton

Developmental Editor
Michelle Ruelos Cannistraci

Production Manager
Larry Main

Art and Design Coordinator
Nicole Reamer

Marketing Coordinator:
Paula Collins

Editorial Assistant:
Amy Tucker

Custom Coordinator
Claudette Corley

NOTICE TO THE READER

Contents

Volume II

AC Fundamentals

The experiments in this manual are designed to accompany *Fundamentals of Electronics: DC/AC Circuits* by David Terrell. The experiments have the same progression and conventions as the text. The experiments start at an introductory level and advance to several different levels of complexity. There are sufficient projects to provide beneficial experiments in any course offering DC or AC circuits.

All beginning and advanced electronics students can benefit from the Manual to accomplish these outcomes:

- test equipment mastery

- use observations to learn and support theory concepts

- learn troubleshooting skills

- improve critical thinking skills (putting several facts together to arrive at a conclusion)

Introductory experiments that introduce how to properly use each piece of test equipment are included as experiments. Oscilloscope introduction including screen pictorials of what the student should see on the oscilloscope are also included in some of the AC circuit experiments.

Organization

The **Objectives** of each experiment are stated to ensure the student understands what is to be learned. The objectives should be reviewed before and after the experiment is completed.

In the **Text Reference**, the textbook reference is given for each experiment. Use the text and look at the referenced material **before** doing an experiment. This will confirm what was learned in theory and aid in writing observations about what was observed while completing procedures.

The **Introduction** will review theory and introduce important concepts that will be learned about how to use the test equipment to accomplish certain procedural steps. Other information within the Introduction will include useful equations and troubleshooting techniques.

The **Procedures** are written for step-by-step guidance in early experiments, in later projects the steps are decreased but are sufficient to ensure the correct conclusions are observed by the student.

The last area of each experiment is the **Observations**. The Observations are practical questions based on the observations made during the course of the experiment. The observations are mixed in with the Procedures to ensure the student uses the circuit to answer questions about circuit operation, and can see what actually happens if circuit parameters change. With this type of observation the student can make the change and directly observe what happens. Rather than answering questions after the circuit has been disconnected or trying to answer the questions outside the lab environment, the questions are presented while the student is working with the circuit in the lab.

Approach

Each series of experiments will have different **Levels**, for instance, in the Series Circuit grouping there are five different levels. In the early levels the Procedures are detailed to provide "step-by-step guidance;" this will create good lab habits. Included in the Procedures are Discussions which are used to ensure that the student knows the right answer and the reason why it is the right answer. This teaches the student to make accurate observations about measurements made in the circuit and proper use of the test equipment. Suggestions on how to follow procedural steps and use equations to calculate or determine circuit values are included in the Discussions areas. Warnings about what could happen if the test equipment is not used properly are also given and emphasized.

It is not necessary that all of the projects be accomplished in a given series. However, each level becomes somewhat more challenging. As the experiments progress in levels and material, fewer procedures are given to guide the student toward the outcome. If each student uses each level correctly, the final level can be accomplished by all students.

This approach is designed to reinforce theory, discover new practical ways of looking at theory, learn to construct circuits and properly use text equipment, and troubleshoot circuits.

When experiments have been completed, allowing students to interact and discuss the results and observations is an important part of any laboratory experience. Encourage this interaction as a means of solidifying information gained from the experiments.

At the end of the Experiments Manual are single sheets of linear and semilog graph paper. Make as many copies of the graph paper as required.

The created graphs and tables could be used in a theory class to enhance visualization of concepts and theories. Having students do an experiment prior to it being presented in theory allows for "discovery" of how things work. Then, the theory can reinforce observations made in the laboratory environment. Additional experiments, using the different levels, can be accomplished in the laboratory, increasing the critical thinking skills of the students.

To the Students

When making "observations," generally there are no wrong answers as long as you write what you observed in accomplishing the procedures. Always try to make as many observations as possible, regardless of how obvious or subtle. State the observations as clearly as you can. Compare your observations with others and discuss them. Add to your list of observations what others have observed, then analyze how they fit or don't fit with yours. Relate the observations to material learned in theory: Are there differences? Are things working contrary to theory? Do your observations support and reinforce theory? Are the graphs and tables the same as discussed in theory?

Create mental images of what you observed, then begin to try to learn **why** it works this way or that way. Ask questions about those things that you do not understand; especially ask **how** or **why** this or that occurred. Doing these things will allow you to benefit from your laboratory experience.

Always preview the text material before doing the experiment. Write down any equations that may assist your completing the experiment. Then read the experiment, doing the calculations before connecting the circuits and measuring them. Carefully follow each procedural step, making sure you understand why the step is being taken. Think about what **should be** observed versus **what is being** observed.

Oscilloscope Introduction: Level I

Name_____ Class_____ Date _____

Objectives   Upon completion of this experiment, you should be able to:

- Determine the function of the basic controls of the oscilloscope.

- Adjust the controls of the oscilloscope to set the zero voltage reference (ground) to a known place on the screen.

- Measure a dc voltage with the aid of the oscilloscope.

Text Reference   Terrell, *Fundamentals of Electronics: DC/AC Circuits*
    Chapter 9, Section 9-7
    Chapter 11, Section 11-6

Materials Required   Variable power supply; 0 to 20 volts dc
    Dual-trace time-based oscilloscope
    Voltmeter
    Appropriate test leads

Introduction

The oscilloscope, commonly known as the O'scope, is the most useful piece of test equipment that a technician can use to analyze and troubleshoot circuits at the component level. The oscilloscope can display the amount of voltage, often referred to as the amplitude or magnitude, and the shape of the voltage.

Most oscilloscopes are dual-trace, meaning that there are two channels and two lines on the screen. This allows two voltages to be observed at the same instant in time. Comparisons of the two voltages can be made in time relation to each other.

This experiment introduces the basic function of the controls and how to use the controls to obtain a stable, viewable voltage waveform or other important information. Future experiments will use the oscilloscope to determine component voltage levels or amplitudes in given circuits.

The written observations about the function of the controls should be detailed enough that they can be used as a reference in future experiments.

Procedures

1. The following controls will be adjusted during the course of this experiment. Find each control on the oscilloscope and check each one off as it is found. If a control cannot be found, check with your instructor or the Oscilloscope Operator's Manual. Some oscilloscopes have different control labels and some controls have combined

operations. If an Operator's Manual is available, the manual will be helpful when learning the controls and their functions.

☐ On/Off switch

☐ Intensity control

☐ Focus control

☐ AC/GND/DC select switch for each channel

☐ Channel 1/A vertical volts per division selector*

☐ Channel 2/B vertical volts per division selector

☐ Channel 1/A vertical position control

☐ Channel 2/B vertical position control

☐ Horizontal position control

☐ Time per division selector

☐ Triggering level

☐ Triggering source

☐ Slope selector or ± polarity switch

☐ Mode select or channel select switch

☐ Calibrate controls for volts/division

☐ Calibrate control for time/division

---

* The 1/A designation refers to Channel 1 or Channel A, whichever the oscilloscope indicates. Therefore, 2/B would be Channel 2 or Channel B.

Notice that the screen has vertical and horizontal lines. These lines are referred to as a graticule. Most graticules have nine horizontal lines creating eight vertical divisions. They may also have eleven vertical lines, creating ten horizontal divisions. Notice the horizontal line in the center of the screen. This line has smaller increments, five smaller divisions between the larger division. If each major division is one, then each smaller increment represents 0.2 divisions.

$$0.2 \times 5 \text{ divisions} = 1$$

Notice that the center vertical line has the same smaller divisions as well. Generally, the center horizontal line will be used as the zero-volt reference line when measuring voltage.

The On/Off switch operation should be obvious and most oscilloscopes have a light that comes on when power is applied.

When **ON**, this oscilloscope has a _____ light that is on.

(color)

2. Set the following controls to the indicated positions.

On/Off . . . . On

Volts/division . . . . 1 volt

AC/GND/DC switch . . . . Gnd

Time/Division* . . . . Mid-range

Mode select switch . . . . Channel 1/A

Vertical position switch . . . . . . Mid-range

Triggering source . . . . Channel 1/A

Triggering mode** . . . . Automatic (Auto)

Horizontal position control . . . . Mid-range

---

* Adjust until a solid line or trace appears across the face of the screen.

** This may be a pull or push operation of the triggering level control knob.

3. There should be a solid horizontal line across the face of the screen. If not, adjust the triggering level control, the vertical position control, or the horizontal position control.

4. Adjust the vertical position control until the trace is in the center of the screen. This line or trace should coincide with the center horizontal line of the graticule.

5. Adjust the **intensity control**, counterclockwise and clockwise, and state your observations about the brightness of the trace. Never leave this control set to maximum intensity for long periods of time. If left in the maximum position, the screen may be damaged. When left unattended the intensity control should be set at the minimum that can be seen.

6. Adjust the **focus control** fully clockwise and counterclockwise and state your observations about the width or clarity of the trace.

7. There are two vertical position controls, one for each channel. Adjust the **vertical position** knob for Channel 1/A slowly clockwise and counterclockwise and state your observations.

8. Adjust the **vertical position control** until the trace is again in the middle of the screen. Now adjust the **horizontal position control** slowly clockwise and counterclockwise and state your observations.

9. The time/division control determines the time it takes for the trace or dot to move one full division on the graticule. Observe the screen and note the number of horizontal divisions from left to right.

Ten divisions total should be noted. There are five divisions on each side of the center vertical line.

Turn the **time/divisions control** counterclockwise to the lowest setting. Observe that the trace has now become a dot and is moving from the left-hand side of the screen to the right-hand side of the screen.

The lowest setting on the time/division control is _____ seconds/division.

Remember that there are 10 horizontal divisions. How long does it take for the trace to go from the left side of the screen to the right side of the screen?

10 divisions × (lowest time/div. setting) = _____

Total time = _____ seconds

10. Set the **time/divisions** setting to 0.5 milliseconds and determine the time required for the trace to go from the left-hand side of the screen to the right-hand side of the screen.

0.5 m sec × 10 divisions = _____m sec

Five milliseconds should be your answer. Each division represents 0.5 milliseconds of time. The left-hand side of the screen represents time zero; the trace will not be at the right-hand side of the screen until 5 milliseconds after the start of the trace. Changes in voltage that occur during this time interval are shown on the screen.

11. The **volts/division control** is used to determine the voltage amplitude that can be displayed on the screen. Notice that the control can be adjusted for different values. At present the **AC/GND/DC select switch** is set on **GND** or zero-volts position. When the switch is in this position, a zero-volt reference line can be established. Set the **vertical position** control so that the trace is in the center of the screen to coincide with the center horizontal line of the graticule.

    Suppose the **volts/division switch** is set on two and the **AC/GND/DC** switch is moved to the **DC** position. Further suppose that the trace moves two divisions upward from the original position. The voltage value indicated will be four volts.

$$2 \text{ divisions} \times 2 \text{ volts/div.} = 4 \text{ volts}$$

    If the trace moves up two divisions, the voltage will be positive. If the trace moves down two divisions, the voltage polarity will be negative.

    Remember the center was zero volts, therefore, if the trace deflects in opposite directions it will indicate different polarities. Think of a number line that is placed in a vertical position.

    Suppose the trace moves up three divisions when the AC/GND/DC switch is moved to DC, with the volts/division selector on 0.2 volts. What is the voltage value being measured?

    (_____ divisions moved) × (_____ volts/div.) = _____ volts

    The value indicated will be +0.6 volts.

Using the Oscilloscope to Measure a DC Voltage

12. Set the following controls to the indicated positions.

    On/Off . . . .   On

    Volts/division . . . .   1 volt

    AC/GND/DC switch . . . .   Gnd

    Time/Division* . . . .   Mid-range

    Mode select switch . . . .   Channel 1/A

    Vertical position switch . . . . . .   Mid-range

    Triggering source . . . .   Channel 1/A

    Triggering mode . . . .   Automatic (Auto)

    Horizontal position control . . . .   Mid-range

    ———————————

    * Adjust until a solid line or trace appears across the face of the screen.

    Make sure the **calibrate control** for the **volts/division control** is turned to the calibrate position. It should be stated near the control which direction the control should be turned to the calibrate position. Some oscilloscopes have lights to indicate that the time/division or the volts/division is out of the calibrate position.

When the controls are not in the calibrate position, the indicated position of the controls is no longer valid. Therefore, in the above example of the 0.6 volt measurement, unless the volts/division was in the calibrate position the actual voltage being measured would not be known.

Adjust the **vertical position control** until a solid trace appears in the center of the screen. When the **AC/GND/DC switch** in the **GND** position, a zero-voltage reference line is established in the center of the screen.

Connect a lead, referred to as the oscilloscope probe, to the Channel 1/A of the oscilloscope.

If using a X10 probe that has a switch that will select X1 or X10, select X1. If the oscilloscope probe does not have a X1 selection and is **only** a X10 probe, divide all the volts/division settings by 10 and set them to this value. If the probe has alligator clips or hook type connectors **do not** divide the volts/division setting by 10.

13. Connect the black ground wire or black hook to the negative side of the dc power supply and the other probe lead to the positive side of the dc power supply.

14. Turn the dc power supply voltage control to minimum and connect the dc voltmeter across the dc power supply.

15. Turn on the dc power supply.

16. Adjust the dc power supply until the dc voltmeter indicates 2 volts. Notice that no change occurred in the oscilloscope trace position.

17. Set the **volts/division selector switch** of Channel 1/A to 2 volts/division position and insure the calibrate control is in the calibrate position.

18. Set the **AC/GND/DC** switch to **DC**.

19. Record the number of divisions the trace moved and the direction it moved.

    Number of divisions moved   _____

    Direction moved, up or down?   _____

20. Multiply the number of divisions moved times the **volts/division setting**.

$$1 \text{ division} \times 2 \text{ volts/division} = 2 \text{ volts}$$

    The voltage measured is positive because the trace moved up.

21. Disconnect the oscilloscope from the dc power supply.

22. Connect the ground or black lead of the probe to the positive output of the dc power supply and connect the probe or the red lead to the negative output of the dc power supply.

23. Turn on the power supply.

24. Determine the voltage indicated by the deflection of the oscilloscope trace.

    DC voltage = _____ volts

    The trace should have deflected down two divisions. Indicating that −2 volts is being measured.

Observations

1. Have your lab partner, other students or the instructor set up unknown dc voltages to measure. Each one correctly completed should be initialed by the individual who set up the unknown dc voltage. Complete as least five.

DC Voltage Measured with the Oscilloscope

DC voltage   _____   Initial   _____

DC voltage   _____   Initial   _____

DC voltage   _____   Initial   _____

DC voltage   _____   Initial   _____

DC voltage   _____   Initial   _____

Oscilloscope: Measuring DC Voltages; Level II

Name _Donivan Mc Greal_ Class _AC Electronics_ Date _12/8/06_
Friday

Objectives Upon completion of this experiment, you should be able to:

- Use the oscilloscope to measure dc voltages in a series circuit.

- Determine the accuracy that dc voltages can be measured, as compared to the VOM or DMM used as a dc voltmeter.

Text Reference Terrell, *Fundamentals of Electronics: DC/AC Circuits*
Chapter 9, Section 9-7
Chapter 11, Section 11-6

Materials Required Variable power supply; 0 to 20 volts dc
Dual-trace oscilloscope
Voltmeter
1-kΩ resistor
2.2-kΩ resistor
3.3-kΩ resistor
Various test leads

Introduction

The oscilloscope can be used as a dc voltmeter. However, just how accurate is the indication? The accuracy will depend on the volts/division setting used and how the voltage level is interpreted by the reader.

Whenever measuring any voltage amplitude or value with the oscilloscope, always use the **lowest** volts/division setting that will not cause the trace to deflect off of the screen. Remember that the zero-volt point can be placed anywhere on the screen by moving the vertical position control with the AC/GND/DC switch in the **GND** position.

Procedures

The following procedures will be written as if the student is using a X1 probe. If using a X10 probe, divide each volts/division setting by 10 and set the volts/division to the number.

Example The procedures call for the volts per division at 5v/division. If using a X10 probe, set the volts/division setting to 0.5v/division.

1. Construct the circuit shown in Figure 28-1. Use the voltmeter to set the power supply voltage to +12 V.

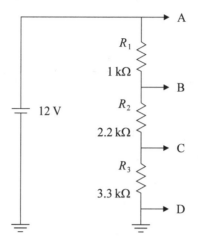

Figure 28-1

2. Set the oscilloscope controls as follows:

Time/division . . . .   mid-range

Volts/division   5

Triggering source . . . .   Channel 1/A, Auto

AC/GND/DC . . . .   GND

3. Set the zero-volt reference line for the center of the screen.

4. Connect the oscilloscope probes to measure the applied voltage. Place the ground lead at Point D and the actual probe at Point A.

Switch the AC/GND/DC control to **DC**.

Discussion The voltage across all three resistors or the applied voltage can also be referred to as V_{AD}. This indicates that the voltage at Point A is measured in reference to Point D. The ground reference point would be Point D.

If measuring V_{AC}, the reference point or zero-volt point will be Point C. The second letter is the common reference point. If there is only one letter, i.e., V_A, then it is assumed that the designated common reference point will be used as the zero-volt point. If no common reference point is designated, the point at which the ground lead of the oscilloscope is placed establishes the common reference point.

---

5. Measure V_{AC} and record the voltage measured with oscilloscope in the appropriate box in Table 28-1.

	OSCILLOSCOPE MEASUREMENTS	VOLTMETER MEASUREMENTS
V_{AD}	11 V_{DC}	+12 V
V_{DA}	-11 V_{DC}	-12 V
V_{AB}	2 V	1.83V
V_{BA}	-2V	-1.83V
V_{BC}	4V	4.09V
V_{CB}	-4V	-4.09V
V_{CD}	6V	6.15V
V_{DC}	-6V	-6.15

Table 28-1

6. Reverse the oscilloscope probe leads and measure V_{DA}. Recording the voltage indication, including polarity, in Table 28-1.

Discussion   When V_{AD} was measured the trace deflected up about 2.4 divisions, which indicates 12 volts positive. If each major division is 5 volts, then each small increment is equal to 1 volt, or

$$0.2 \times 5 \text{ volts} = 1 \text{ volt}$$

Notice that there are 5 small increments in each major division. Therefore, each small increment indicates 0.2. If the trace had deflected one small increment higher, then the total deflection would have been 2.6 divisions or an indication of 13 volts. To determine the voltage indication take the number of divisions the trace deflected and multiply it by the volts/division setting.

$$\textit{\# of divisions} \times \text{volts/division setting}$$

$$2.4 \text{ divisions} \times 5 \text{ volts/division} = 12 \text{ volts}$$

or

$$2.6 \text{ divisions} \times 5 \text{ volts/division} = 13 \text{ volts}$$

Notice that when V_{DA} was measured the trace deflected down 2.4 divisions. This indicates that the polarity is negative. This change in polarity occurred for the same reason that the polarity changes when you are using a VOM or DMM to measure the voltage when the reference point changes.

---

7. Place the oscilloscope probe leads to measure V_{AB}.

Discussion   Notice that the amount of deflection is not a complete division. It is difficult to determine the actual value of the deflection.

Change the volts/division setting to 1 volt/division. State the difference between this setting and the volts/division of 5.

Change the volts/division setting to 0.5. State which volts/division is easier to use to determine the voltage.

8. Using the 0.5 volts/division setting, determine V_{AB} and record the indication in Table 28-1.

9. Reverse the oscilloscope probe leads and measure V_{BA} and record the value in Table 28-1.

Discussion   The deflection should have been about 3.8 divisions, which means that the indication is approximately 1.9 volts for both measurements. When the deflection goes up, a positive voltage is indicated; when the deflection goes down a negative voltage is indicated.

10. Without changing the volts/division control (0.5 v/division), connect the oscilloscope probe leads to measure V_{BC}.

Discussion   Notice that the trace deflected off the screen. This indicates that the volts/division setting is too small.

11. Slowly increase the volts/division setting until the trace is on the screen and the deflection can be measured. Use the smallest deflection per division that can be used.

Discussion   The lowest volts/division setting that can be used is probably 2 volts/division, with a total deflection of a little over two divisions. It would indicate about +4 volts.

12. Record the indicated V_{BC} value in Table 28-1.

13. Using the same volts/division sitting, measure V_{CB} and record the value in Table 28-1.

14. Switch the AC/GND/DC to **GND**. Adjust the vertical position control until the trace is one division above the bottom of the screen or on the 2nd horizontal line from the bottom of the screen.

Discussion   By changing the zero reference point on the screen, the trace can deflect seven divisions up before it goes off the screen.

This will allow for larger voltages to be measured and still use a smaller volts/division setting.

15. Place the AC/GND/DC setting in the **DC** position.

    Change the volts/division setting to 1 volt/division, placing the oscilloscope probe leads to measure V_{CD}.

    Indicate the number of divisions of deflection ___a ble c r___

16. Determine the voltage indication and record the value in Table 28-1.

17. Place the AC/GND/DC switch in the **GND** position and adjust the vertical position control until the trace is one division from the top of the screen.

18. Connect the oscilloscope probe leads to measure V_{DC}.

    Place the AC/GND/DC switch in the **DC** position, determine the voltage indication, and record the value in Table 28-1.

19. Using the voltmeter, measure each voltage indicated in Table 28-1.

    State your observations about the comparisons noted in the measurements made with the oscilloscope and the voltmeter.

    The oscilloscope displays a comparison in wave form whereas the voltmeter displays a numerical value

Observations

1. If the trace deflects up when measuring a dc voltage, the polarity of the voltage is ___positive___.

2. If the trace deflects for 2.6 divisions downward from the zero reference point when the volts/division control is set on 1 volt/division, what voltage is being indicated?

    -2.6 volts

3. If the zero reference point is in the center of the screen and the volts/division control is on 2 volt/division, what is the maximum positive voltage that can be measured and have the trace remain on the screen.

    + 20 volts

4. If -10 volts is to be measured and the zero reference point is in the center of the screen, what is the lowest volts/division setting that can be used and have the trace remain on the screen.

2 volts/division

5. Refer to Figure 28-1. If V_{AC} is being measured, the ground lead of the oscilloscope probe will be placed at ____.

   a. the top of R_1

   b. the bottom of R_1

   c. the bottom of R_2

   d. the top of R_2

Oscilloscope: Single Reference Point Measurements; Level III

Name_____ Class_____ Date _____

Objectives   Upon completion of this experiment, you should be able to:

- Measure dc voltages with the oscilloscope in a complex circuit, with a single common reference point.

- Review resistive series-parallel concepts, including Kirchhoff's Voltage Law.

Text Reference   Terrell, *Fundamentals of Electronics: DC/AC Circuits*
    Chapter 9, Section 9-7
    Chapter 11, Section 11-6

Materials Required   Variable power supply; 0 to 20 volts dc
    Dual-trace oscilloscope
    820-Ω resistor
    1-kΩ resistors (2)
    2.2-kΩ resistors (2)
    3.3-kΩ resistors (2)
    Various test leads

Introduction

In almost all "real world" circuits, a single common reference point exists. This common reference point could be earth ground or a chassis ground. In either case, all voltages must be measured in reference to this common point.

When using the oscilloscope, the ground lead of the oscilloscope is earth ground, unless some means is used to isolate the oscilloscope from earth ground. Therefore, oscilloscope probes cannot be placed across a component that is ungrounded because a new ground or reference point would be created. Creating more than one ground point in the circuit could cause fuses to open and power supplies could become damaged. There cannot be more that one common reference voltage supply point in a circuit. Therefore, when measuring an ungrounded component in a circuit, some other technique must be used to measure the voltage across this component when using an oscilloscope. Several methods can be employed; this experiment covers just one such method. Other techniques will be practiced in future experiments as more information is gained about the oscilloscope.

Procedures

1. Calculate the voltage drops across each resistor in the circuit shown in Figure 29-1 and record each value in Table 29-1.

RESISTOR	RESISTOR VOLTAGE
R_1	
R_2	
R_3	
R_4	
R_5	
R_6	

Table 29-1

2. Construct the circuit shown in Figure 29-1, using the oscilloscope to set the power supply voltage (the voltage at Point A with reference to Point F).

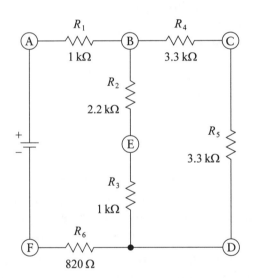

Figure 29-1

3. Connect the ground lead of the oscilloscope to Point F. Do not move this lead unless instructed to do so.

   Adjust the zero-volt reference line for the center of the screen by following the procedures learned in the previous experiments. Adjust the volts/division control that will allow for the most accurate measurement. Make sure the AC/GND/DC switch is in the **GND** position when adjusting for a zero-volt center, then place the AC/GND/DC switch in the **DC** position.

4. Measure the voltage at Point A and adjust the voltage to as close to 18 volts as possible.

5. Measure the voltage at Point F and record the value in Table 29-2.

Discussion   This value should have been zero volts. This indicates that this is the zero reference point and the "ground" for this circuit.

POINT	VOLTAGE
V_F	
V_D	
V_C	
V_E	
V_B	
V_A	+18 V

Table 29-2

6. Measure the voltage at Point D and record this value in Table 29-2. This measurement is the voltage across R_6. Is this value comparable to the calculated value in Table 29-1?

$V_{R_6} = $ _____ volts

Discussion   The determined value for R_6 should be about 5.1 volts. The oscilloscope leads should be in parallel with R_6 when measuring Point D.

7. Measure the voltage at Point C and record this value in Table 29-2.

Discussion   The value measured at Point C is the sum of the voltages across R_6 and R_5. To determine the voltage across R_5, subtract the voltage measured at Point D from the voltage measured at Point C.

$$V_D - V_C = V_{R_5}$$

$V_{R_5} = $ _____ volts

This voltage difference should be about 3.4 volts. See if this voltage difference is comparable to the calculated value for resistor R_5 in Table 29-1.

8. Measure the voltage at Point E and record this value in Table 29-2.

Discussion   This voltage value represents the sum of the voltages across R_6 and R_3. The voltage across R_3 can be determined by subtracting the voltage measured at Point D from the voltage measured at Point E.

$$V_E - V_D = V_{R_3}$$

$V_{R_3} =$ _____ volts

The voltage at Point E should be about 11.8 volts and the voltage across R_3 should be about 6.7 volts.

---

9. Measure the voltage at Point B and record this value in Table 29-2.

Discussion   The voltage at Point B represents several voltages values.

$$V_{R_6} + V_{R_5} + V_{R_4} = V_B$$

$$V_{R_6} + V_{R_3} + V_{R_2} = V_B$$

$$V_C + V_{R_4} = V_B$$

$$V_E + V_{R_2} = V_B$$

$$V_A - V_{R_1} = V_B$$

---

10. Using the voltage equations listed above and the previously measured points and determined voltage drops, determine the following resistor voltage drops.

$V_{R_2} =$ _____ volts

$V_{R_4} =$ _____ volts

$V_{R_1} =$ _____ volts

11. Add the measured voltage drops across the following resistors to determine if they are equal to the applied voltage.

R_1, R_2, R_3, and R_6

Total voltage value = _____ volts

Add the measured voltage drops across the following resistors to determine if they are equal to the applied voltage.

R_1, R_4, R_5, and R_6

Total voltage value = _____ volts

12. State why R_1 and R_6 were used in both determinations. Draw current paths to prove your answer.

Observations

1. State in your own words the technique used to measure the voltage drop across an ungrounded component. (*Hint:* voltage is the difference of potential between two points.)

2. If the ground lead of the oscilloscope is moved to Point D, state what two voltage points will be measured to determine the voltage drop across R_2.

To prove your answer, move the ground lead of the oscilloscope to Point D and measure the points indicated by your answer.

3. If the ground lead of the oscilloscope is moved to Point D, is the polarity of the voltage across R_6 the same as when the ground lead was at point F?

Prove your answer by measuring the voltage at point F with respect to Point D.

$V_{FD} = $ _____ volts

Oscilloscope: Another Technique; Level IV

Name_____ Class_____ Date_____

Objectives   Upon completion of this experiment, you should be able to:

- Use the subtract (A-B) or (2-1) function of the oscilloscope in a circuit with one common reference point.

- Discover what occurs if a circuit has more than one common reference point.

Text Reference   Terrell, *Fundamentals of Electronics: DC/AC Circuits*
     Chapter 9, Section 9-7
     Chapter 11, Section 11-6

Materials Required   Variable power supply; 0 to 20 volts dc
Dual-trace oscilloscope
1-kΩ resistor
2.2-kΩ resistor
3.3-kΩ resistor
Various test leads

Introduction

The two channels for the oscilloscope are generally called Channel 1 and Channel 2 or Channel A and Channel B. To avoid confusion, this experiment will refer to Channel 1 and Channel 2. Channel 1 will be the channel of the oscilloscope that can be inverted and Channel 2 will be the channel that is not inverted.

Oscilloscopes generally have a position on the mode switch that will allow Channel 1 and Channel 2 to be added together. If Channel 1 is inverted and the mode switch is set on **add**, the oscilloscope will subtract Channel 1 from Channel 2. In the last experiment the subtraction was accomplished by hand. The oscilloscope has the capability to do this process.

Check your oscilloscope to determine: (*Check off which of those that apply.*)

If the mode switch has a add position?	__ yes	__ no
If Channel 1 can be inverted?	__ yes	__ no
If Channel 2 can be inverted?	__ yes	__ no
If the mode switch has a subtract position?	__ yes	__ no

How you answered the questions will determine the set-up that is needed to accomplish the subtraction function.

If the oscilloscope has an **add** position only, then one channel can be inverted. If the oscilloscope has a subtract or A-B or 2-1 position, then no channel needs to be inverted. The oscilloscope will do it automatically.

The channel that can be inverted will be referred to as **Channel 1** and the channel that is not inverted will be referred to as **Channel 2**. This will make it easier to determine which channel to subtract from which channel.

Channel 2 minus Channel 1 equals the voltage being measured.

When the A-B or 2-1 function is needed in a later experiment, you may need to refer back to this experiment and review the procedures to accomplish the task.

Procedures

1. Set the oscilloscope controls as follows:

   AC/GND/DC . . . .   GND (both channels)

   Time base control . . . .   0.5m sec

   Volts/division . . . .   5 volts/division (both channels)

   Mode control . . . .   dual

   Triggering source . . . .   Channel 1, Auto

2. Adjust the vertical positioning controls until both traces are in the center of the screen, establishing the zero reference points.

3. Construct the circuit shown in Figure 30-1.

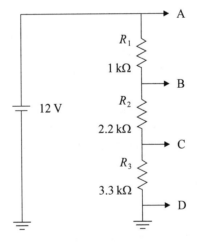

Figure 30-1

4. Use **Channel 2**, the channel that does not get inverted, to connect to Point A and Point D in order to adjust the dc power supply for 12 volts.

5. Connect **Channel 1**, the channel that gets inverted, to Point B and Point D, where Point D is the common reference point.

   ⚡CAUTION Make sure both ground leads of the oscilloscope are attached to Point D.

6. How many divisions did **Channel 2** deflect when the AC/GND/DC switch was placed in the **DC** position?

_____ divisions

How many divisions did **Channel 1** deflect?

_____ divisions

7. Subtract the number of divisions:

(**Channel 2** divisions) – (**Channel 1** divisions)

_____ divisions

Now, multiply the difference between the divisions by the volts/division setting (5 volts/division).

_____ volts

This is the voltage drop across R_1.

Discussion   This is a demonstration of what the oscilloscope does when the subtract (A-B) or (2-1) function is selected. The zero reference lines were at the same point and the volts/division controls were on the same number.

---

8. Move **Channel 2**, non-inverted channel, to Point B and **Channel 1**, the inverted channel, to Point C.

State which resistor(s) are being measured by **Channel 2**.

State which resistor(s) are being measured by **Channel 1**.

Discussion   The voltage drops across R_2 and R_3 are being measured by **Channel 2**. The voltage drop across R_3 is being measured by **Channel 1**. Therefore, the difference between what the two channels are measuring is the voltage drop across R_2.

---

9. Subtract the voltage measured by **Channel 1** from the voltage being measured by **Channel 2**.

_____ volts

This represents the voltage across R_2.

10. With this information, determine the voltage drop across R_3.

    _____ volts

11. Place the AC/GND/DC switch of both channels in the **GND** position. Make sure the zero reference line for both channels is the same and that the volts/division control is on the same number.

12. Move the mode select switch to **add**. There are some oscilloscopes where the dual control must be turned off in order to use the add function. Therefore, turn off the dual selected switch. Invert the channel that can be inverted.

13. Place the AC/GND/DC control of both channels to the **DC** position.

14. Determine the divisions that the trace deflects.

    _____ divisions

    Multiply the number of divisions of deflection by the volts/division setting.

    Compare the answer determined in Step 9 to the value obtained in this step.

15. Move the oscilloscope probe at Point B to Point C and move the probe at Point C to Point B.

    State your observations about the voltage level and polarity measured in each step.

16. Move the oscilloscope probes to measure the voltage across R_1 and indicate the voltage measured. Compare this voltage to the value obtained in Step 7.

Discussion   Think of Channel 2 as the red lead of a voltmeter and Channel 1 as the black lead of a voltmeter.

---

17. Place the mode switch in the dual position and place the invert switch so that **Channel 1** is no longer inverted.

18. Place the ground lead of Channel 1 at Point B.

    Place the ground lead of Channel 2 at Point D.

    Place the Channel 1 probe at Point A and record the voltage being measured.

    _____ volts

    Place the probe for Channel 2 at Point C and indicate the voltage across R_3.

    _____ volts

State your observation about the two voltages measured and state why you think the voltages are as indicated.

Discussion It seems there are two grounds in the circuit. There are 12 volts across R_1 and zero volts across R_3. To prove this use the Channel 2 probe to measure the voltage at Point B.

This indicates that there can be only one zero-volt reference point in a circuit when using an oscilloscope. All oscilloscope ground leads must be placed at the same point in the circuit.

Observations

1. State in your own words how to measure the voltage across R_2 in Figure 30-1. Use the subtract function of the oscilloscope.

AC Introduction: Drawing a Sine Wave; Level I

Name_____ Class_____ Date _____

Objectives	Upon completion of this experiment, you should be able to:

- Observe a sine function on a graph.
- Determine the period for a sine wave.
- Determine the frequency of a sine wave.
- Determine the peak-to-peak value of a sine wave.
- Determine the peak value of a sine wave.
- Determine the instantaneous voltage value on a sine wave.

Text Reference	Terrell, *Fundamentals of Electronics: DC/AC Circuits* Chapter 11, Sections 11-1 and 11-2
Material Required	Scientific calculator

Introduction

A sine wave can be represented by taking the sine of every angle between 0° and 360° and plotting it on a graph of degrees versus amplitude. The sine function can be used to draw a curve that represents an alternating voltage or current. The sine wave can be displayed on the oscilloscope screen as a function of amplitude versus time.

Using this graphical representation of a sine wave, the period (or time) for one complete cycle of the sine wave can be determined. This representation will also be used to measure the amplitude of the voltage waveform. The amplitude of the alternating voltage or current can be measured in several ways; peak, peak-to-peak, RMS (root mean square), or an instantaneous value (voltage amplitude at an instant in time).

The period for one complete cycle can be used to determine the frequency or the number of complete cycles that will occur in one second. This is the form that is used when referring to an alternating current (ac) or voltage.

Procedures

1. Determine the sine (calculator in degrees) of each angle listed in Table 31-1.

DEGREES	SINE OF ANGLE
15°	
30°	
45°	
60°	
75°	
90°	
105°	
120°	
135°	
150°	
165°	
180°	
195°	
210°	
225°	
240°	
255°	
270°	
285°	
300°	
315°	
330°	
345°	
360°	

Table 31-1

2. Observe Table 31-1 and the sines of the angles. State your observations about the different angles and their sines. Make as many observations as possible. Then compare the list with other lab teams to see who can come up with the most accurate and longest list of observations.

Discussion   The observations should have included the following:

Which angles have the same sines (complementary angles).

Why some sines have a positive value and others have negative value, but they both have the same absolute values (reference angles).

---

3. Observe the graph paper provided at the end of this experiment. Notice that each of the angles in Table 31-1 is along the center horizontal axis of the graph. Each major division represents 15°. The horizontal axis can also be used to measure time.

Observe the vertical axis. Each division is equal to 0.125 units. It takes eight divisions to equal one unit.

Plot each sine value from Table 31-1 on the graph. All positive sines will go above the center line and all negative sines will be below the center line. Try to be as accurate as possible when selecting the vertical points on the graph.

4. Connect each selected point with a smooth solid line.

Observe Figure 11-3 on page 702 of the text and compare the results on your graph to the graph in the text.

Discussion   The graph paper should have one complete cycle of a sine wave. It should cover the entire page, moving horizontally from left to right, and should go up eight vertical divisions and down eight vertical divisions.

The graph should include 24 horizontal divisions. These 24 divisions represent the **time** for one complete cycle of the sine wave. The time for one complete cycle of the sine wave is referred to as the period. If the period is known, the number of cycles that occur in one second (time reference) can be determined. The measurement of how many complete cycles that occur in one second is referred to as the frequency, measured in Hertz (Hz). When the period is known, the frequency is determined by establishing the following ratio:

$$(period) \times (F) = (1\ sec) \times (1\ cycle)$$

Where **F** is the number of cycles that occur in one second.

or

$$F = \frac{1}{period}$$

As an example, suppose each division on the graph represents 1 millisecond. There are 24 divisions, therefore the period is equal to:

$$period = 24 \text{ div.} \times 1 \text{ msec}$$

$$24 \text{ msec} = 24 \text{ div.} \times 1 \text{ msec}$$

The frequency is then:

$$\frac{1}{24 \text{ msec}} = 41.67 \text{ Hz}$$

Using this procedure, the frequency of a sine wave can be determined.

Procedures for Finding the Frequency Using the Oscilloscope:

- Determine the number of divisions for one complete cycle of the sine wave.

- Look at the time/division setting of the oscilloscope.

- Multiply the number of divisions for one complete cycle by the time/division setting of the oscilloscope. This determines the period.

- Take the reciprocal or divide the period into 1, for the number of cycles per second or Hertz.

Example

Time/division setting of 0.2 msec

Divisions for one complete cycle; 24

The period is:

$$0.2 \text{ msec} \times 24 = 4.8 \text{ msec}$$

The frequency is:

$$\frac{1}{4.8 \text{ msec}} = 208.33 \text{ Hz}$$

5. Determine the frequency of the graph, if the time/division setting is 0.5 msec.

Discussion   The frequency should have been 83.33 Hz or 83.33 complete cycles in one second.

The amplitude of the waveform is determined by the number of divisions the waveform goes up or down from a given point. The center of the graph will represent zero volts. Notice that the sines of 0°, 180°, and 360° are zero. A true sine wave must pass through zero at these points.

From our reference point (the center of the graph), how many divisions does the graph go up to its maximum point?

From our reference point, how many divisions does the graph go down to its maximum point.

Armed with this information, the positive and negative peak amplitudes or voltages can be determined. If this waveform appeared on the oscilloscope and the volts/division setting of the oscilloscope is known, simply multiply the volts\division setting by the number of divisions.

Example   Suppose the volts/divisions setting of the oscilloscope is 5 volts\division.

The number of vertical divisions from the reference line to the upper most point is 8 divisions.

Therefore, the most positive voltage point is:

8 divisions × 5 volts/division = 40 volts peak

Because we stated that the voltage is a peak value, it is understood that it is the most positive voltage of the sine wave. It is also known that this is a positive value because we went up from the center line.

Determine the negative peak value, if the volts/division setting is still 5 volts\division.

Notice that the absolute value of the positive peak value and the negative peak value are equal. If we have a true sine wave, this will **always** be true.

6. Determine the positive and negative peak values of the sine wave if the volts/division setting is 0.2 volts\division.

7. How many division are there between the positive peak value and the negative peak value?

Discussion   This measurement is referred to as the peak-to-peak value. The same procedure for determining the peak value is used to determine the peak-to-peak value: multiplying the number of divisions between the most positive value and the most negative value by the volts/division setting of the oscilloscope.

8. Determine the peak-to-peak value of the sine wave on the graph if the volts/division setting is 5 volts\division.

Discussion   The peak-to-peak value in Step 7 should have been 80 volts peak-to-peak. It is sometimes easier to determine the peak-to-peak value and then determine the peak value by dividing by 2.

Observe the graph and notice that any voltage value can be determined by measuring the number of divisions from the reference point and then multiplying this number by the volts/division setting of the oscilloscope.

Example   Note the number of divisions that are between the reference line and the graph at 30°. The vertical indication is 0.5 because the sine of 30° is 0.5. This indicates that the voltage at 30° will be one-half the peak voltage. Or, the voltage at any point on the graph is equal to:

sine of the angle multiplied by the peak value

$$\sin \angle \times Vpk = V_{inst}$$

9. The volts/division setting is 5 volts\division. Determine the V_{inst} value at 45°.

Answer $\sin 45° \times 40 \text{ V} = 28.28 \text{ V}$

10. Determine the following voltage values at the indicated angles. Use the graph for a reference.

135° with a volts/division setting of 1 volt\division

225° with a volts/division setting of 0.2 volts/division

240° with a volts/division setting of 10 volts/division

Observations

1. State in your own words the definition of the following terms and describe how to measure or calculate each of the values:

   Period

   Frequency

   Peak voltage

Peak-to-peak voltage

Instantaneous value of voltage

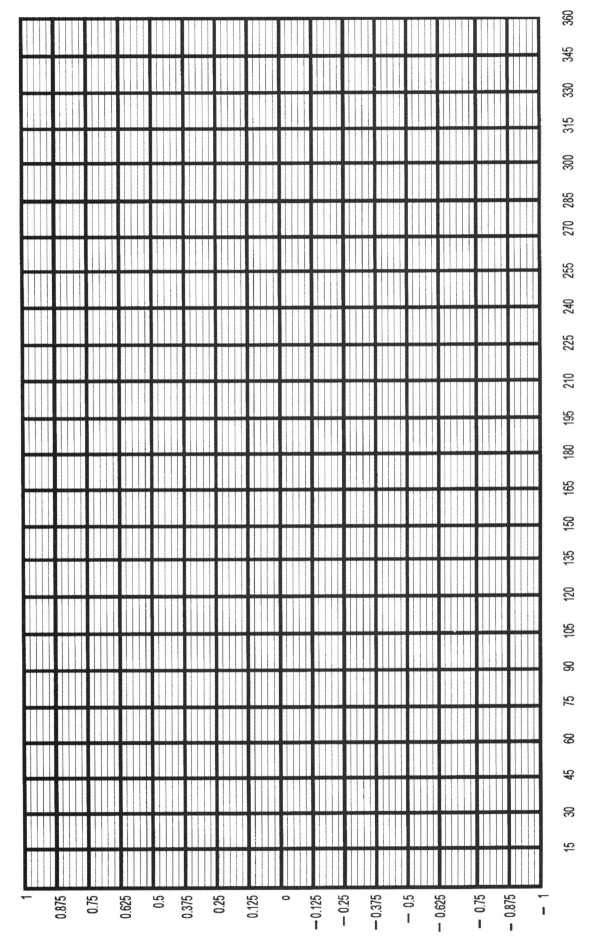

Alternating Voltage: Measuring an AC Voltage; Level II

Name_____ Class_____ Date _____

Objectives	Upon completion of this experiment, you should be able to:

- Use the Function Generator.
- Measure ac voltage amplitudes and frequency with the oscilloscope.

Text Reference Terrell, *Fundamentals of Electronics: DC/AC Circuits*
    Chapter 1, Sections 11-2 and 11-6

Materials Required Dual-trace oscilloscope
Function Generator or Signal Generator
Ohmmeter
DMM—AC voltmeter
Various test leads

Introduction

Function Generator The Function Generator produces several types of output waveforms. In later experiments, nonsinusoidal waveforms will be observed. For the purposes of this experiment, only the sine wave function of the generator will be explored.

The Operator's Manual for the Function Generator will be helpful in determining how the generator operates.

Procedures

1. Find the following controls on the function generator.

   Frequency range switch(s) or coarse adjustment _____

   Frequency adjust or fine adjustment   _____

   Voltage or amplitude adjustment*   _____

   _____

   * This control may have two types of adjustments: low voltage and high voltage. Pull out for low voltage; push in for high voltage.

   _____

   Discussion For the purposes of this experiment, consider the frequency indication of the generator to be nonexistent. Normally a **standard** test instrument has to be selected to measure all values. A standard is the measurement device which is considered to be accurate at all times. This prevents errors between measurement devices. In this way all errors are the same percentage. The oscilloscope is the standard for this experiment.

Earth Ground   The Function Generator has a ground lead that will be connected to earth ground. This means that when the ground lead of the generator is connected in the circuit, an earth ground or constant zero reference point is created. When using the oscilloscope and the function generator, the ground leads of the oscilloscope probes and the ground lead of the function generator must be connected together.

The range selection switches generally do exactly that; they select a range of frequencies within which the generator will operate. In most cases the range selector will indicate mid-range of the possible frequencies.

The function generator may have other switches; some may say percent duty cycle, pulse width, and so on. Make sure that these switches are in the calibrate or 100% position so as not to interfere with the sine wave.

Another switch could be a DC offset switch. If this switch has an off position make sure it is off. If it does not have an off position, adjust it for about mid-range.

2. Connect the ohmmeter between the ground lead of the function generator and the ground lead of the oscilloscope. Then connect the ohmmeter between an earth ground connection and the ground lead of the oscilloscope or the function generator.

State your observations.

3. Set the oscilloscope controls as follows:

Time/division	0 msec
Volts/division	1 volt/division
Slope	+ (positive)
Mode	Channel A/1
Trigger source	Channel A/1 (Auto)
AC/GND/DC	GND

Adjust the vertical positioning knob until the zero-volt reference point is in the center of the screen, making sure the volts/division calibrate control and the time/division calibrate control are in the calibrate position.

4. Set the generator controls as follows:

Range selection	1 k
Frequency adjust	mid-range
Amplitude control (high)	mid-range

5. Connect the oscilloscope probes to the function generator leads.

   Set the AC/GND/DC switch to **AC**.

6. Adjust the frequency control knob of the function generator until approximately one complete cycle appears on the face of the screen.

7. Adjust the triggering level control on the oscilloscope slowly clockwise and counterclockwise. State your observations.

Discussion The amplitude control of the function generator might need to be adjusted to create a stable trace on the screen.

After a stable trace is observed notice that where the trace begins varies as the triggering level control is adjusted. The control adjusts the amount of voltage required to initiate the trace. Normally, we want to adjust this control until the trace just starts on the zero-volt reference line. Remember that this point represents the 0° point of the sine wave. The waveform being viewed should look very similar to the waveform drawn in Experiment 31.

---

8. Adjust the triggering level control until the traces start on the left side of the screen at the zero-volt reference line. Adjust the function generator frequency control until one complete cycle covers the ten (10) horizontal divisions on the screen.

   When the sine wave is in this position on the screen, we will refer to it as the **standard position.**

9. Adjust the function generator amplitude control until the maximum peak point is 3 divisions upward from the zero-volt reference point and 3 divisions downward from the zero-volt reference point, with the oscilloscope volts/division setting at 1 volt/division.

10. Determine the time for one complete cycle.

    _____ divisions × _____ (time/division) = _____ seconds

    Determine the actual frequency of the waveform.

    _____ Hz

11. Determine the peak-to-peak value of voltage.

    _____ divisions × _____ (volts/division) = _____ V pk-to-pk

---

Discussion The frequency should be 1 kHz at 6 V pk-to-pk

12. Determine the peak voltage of the waveform.

    _____ V pk

Discussion   There are 10 divisions for a complete cycle. This means that 360° is spread out over 10 divisions or 36° per division. Zero degrees starts at the lefthand side and 180° is in the center of the screen—5 divisions times 36° equals 180°.

Notice the small increments between each division; each of these is equal to 7.2°.

---

13. Determine the voltage at 72° by:

    Determining the number of divisions from 0° to 72°.

$$\frac{72°}{36° \text{ per division}} = 2 \text{ divisions}$$

Move to the right two divisions and find the number of vertical divisions at this point. The number of vertical divisions should be about 2.8 to 2.9 divisions.

Multiply the number of divisions by the volts/division setting on the oscilloscope.

$$2.8 \text{ division} \times 1 \text{ volts/division} = 2.8 \text{ V}$$

Remember, this is an instantaneous value of voltage.

14. Determine the instantaneous value of voltage at 150°.

    _____ horizontal divisions

    _____ vertical divisions

    _____ volts

15. Cover the frequency indication on the function generator.

    Set the oscilloscope time/division control to 50 μsec/div. and adjust the function generator frequency control until two (2) complete cycles of a sine wave are displayed on the screen.

    If necessary adjust the oscilloscope triggering level control until the trace starts in the standard position.

16. Determine the number of divisions per complete cycle.

    _____ Divisions

    Determine the period for the sine wave.

    _____ Period

    Determine the frequency.

    _____ Hz

17. Did the peak value of voltage change?

18. Adjust the oscilloscope time/division control to 0.1 msec/div.

    On which setting of the oscilloscope time/division setting is it easier to determine the period of the sine wave?

    Adjust the oscilloscope volts/division setting to 5 volts/division.

    On which setting of the oscilloscope volts/division control is it easier to determine the 3 volts peak amplitude?

Discussion   Try to make the display as large as possible when measuring voltage or time.

Setting a Frequency   When the frequency is known and the function generator must be set to the known frequency, the process is reversed.

   Determine the period for the frequency.

   Divide the period by the number of divisions desired.

   Adjust the oscilloscope time/division control to the determined value or the next higher value.

Example   Frequency = 8 kHz
             Period = 0.125 msec
             Divide period by 10 = 12.5 μsec
             Set oscilloscope time/divisions to 20 μsec
             The number of divisions per complete cycle is 6.25 divisions.

---

19. Adjust the function generator frequency control until the time for one complete cycle is as close as possible to 6.25 divisions, with the oscilloscope time/divisions setting at 20 μsec/div.

    Observe the frequency indication of the function generator. Does it indicate exactly 8 kHz?

Discussion   The two indications should be close, but they are probably not the same. This is why a standard is selected.

   The output voltage amplitude should still be 3 volts peak. If not, readjust the amplitude control until it is at this level.

   Although the oscilloscope will not indicate the RMS voltage, it can be determined by multiplying the peak value by 0.707. However, the DMM, when measuring an ac voltage, will indicate the RMS value. There is a problem when using the DMM to measure an ac voltage. Depending on the DMM, it has a limit on the maximum frequency that can be measured accurately. The Operator's Manual for the DMM will state the maximum frequency limit.

---

20. Measure the function generator output voltage with the DMM on ac volts.

    _____ indicated value

Multiply 3 V pk times 0.707 = 2.1 V RMS

State your observations about the accuracy of the DMM measurement of the RMS voltage.

21. Set the function generator frequency to 10 kHz, using the oscilloscope as the standard. Use the **Setting the Frequency** procedures outlined in Step 18.

    Make sure the oscilloscope indicates 3 V pk.

    Measure the RMS voltage using the DMM.

    DMM indication _____ volts

22. Set the function generator frequency to 100 kHz, using the oscilloscope as the standard. Adjust the function generator amplitude adjustment until the oscilloscope measures 5 V pk.

    Determine the RMS value, using the oscilloscope indication.

    _____ V RMS

    Measure the function generator output voltage, using the DMM.

    DMM indication _____

    Is the DMM indication accurate?

    State your observations about measuring an ac voltage at higher frequencies with a DMM versus the oscilloscope.

Observations

1. Have another lab team or lab members set up unknown voltage and frequency values for practice in measurement.

                                   Practice

    Frequency #1 _____ at _____ V pk

    Frequency #2 _____ at _____ V pk

    Frequency #3 _____ at _____ V pk

AC Voltage: Measuring AC in a Resistive Series Circuit; Level III

Name _____   Class _____   Date _____

Objectives   Upon completion of this experiment, you should be able to:

• Measure frequency at a specified voltage amplitude, using the oscilloscope.

• Measure an ac voltage in a resistive series circuit, using the oscilloscope, with one common reference point (ground).

• Observe the accuracy of the DMM, measuring a RMS voltage at higher frequencies.

• Observe the effect that changing frequencies has on the voltage drops across resistors.

• Use the subtraction function (2-1) of the oscilloscope to measure ungrounded components.

Text   Terrell, *Fundamentals of Electronics: DC/AC Circuits*
Reference   Chapter 11, Section 11-2 and 11-6
              Chapter 6

Materials   Function generator
Required   Dual-trace oscilloscope
          1-kΩ resistor
          2.2-kΩ resistor
          3.3-kΩ resistor
          DMM
          Various test leads

Introduction

When the ground lead of the function generator is placed in the circuit an earth ground point is created. This point automatically becomes the common reference point. The oscilloscope ground leads **must** be placed at this point in order to avoid having two zero reference points in one circuit. The ground lead of the oscilloscope is also earth ground and must be placed at the same point as the function generator ground lead in order to get accurate voltage measurements.

The channel of the oscilloscope that is inverted will become the common lead when measuring ungrounded components. The add-invert function can be used to measure the voltage drops across any ungrounded component.

To determine the period of a sine wave, multiply the number of divisions for one complete cycle by the time/division setting of the oscilloscope. To determine the frequency, take the reciprocal of the period.

To determine the peak voltage value of the sine wave, multiply the number of divisions from the zero reference line of the oscilloscope to the most positive or negative amplitude by the volts/division setting of the oscilloscope. The peak-to-peak value can be measured by determining the number of divisions between the most negative amplitude and the most positive amplitude and multiplying this by the volts/division setting of the oscilloscope.

The oscilloscope is the standard measurement device and the all measured voltages and frequencies are referenced to the oscilloscope.

The DMM will only measure the RMS value of an ac sine wave.

Procedures

1. Using Figure 33-1 as a reference, calculate the values listed in Table 33-1. List all ac voltage values in peak-to-peak.

	CALCULATED VALUE
I_{Total}	
R_{Total}	
V_{R_1}	
V_{R_2}	
V_{R_3}	

Table 33-1

If the voltage used to determine current is in peak-to-peak, the current is also in peak-to-peak.

2. Construct the circuit shown in Figure 33-1.

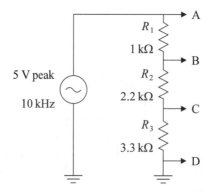

Figure 33-1

Discussion   The period for 10 kHz is 0.1 milliseconds. Divide the period by 10. The time/division setting of the oscilloscope should be 10 microseconds if one complete cycle for 10 divisions is desired.

An easy way to measure peak -to-peak: Adjust the vertical position control until the negative peak amplitude sits on a horizontal line, then count the number of divisions up from that point to the positive peak amplitude. Multiply the number of divisions by the volts/division setting on the oscilloscope. If the volts/division setting of the oscilloscope is 2 volts/division, then 5 divisions would equal 10 volts peak-to-peak or 5 volts peak.

Measure the input voltage, Point A, when the function generator is connected to the circuit. Another good practice, is to monitor the input voltage as the frequency is changed to maintain a constant input voltage.

It is not always necessary to have the time/division or volts/division on the exact setting stated in the experiment. The settings are suggestions. If it is easier on other settings, use them. When **not** using the subtract function (A-B) or (2-1), it is not necessary to have both channels set on the same volts/division. If it is easier to measure voltage amplitudes on other settings, use them. Always try to spread the sine wave out, making it as large as possible and easier to measure more accurately.

3. Using the channel that inverts, measure the peak-to-peak voltage at Point C, V_{R_3}, and record it in Table 33-2.

COMPONENT	VOLTAGE VALUE
R_1	
R_2	
R_3	

Table 33-2

4. By placing the probe of the channel that does not invert at Point B, the voltages across which two resistors are being measured?

_____ and _____

What is the peak-to-peak voltage value measured at this point?

_____ volts peak-to-peak

5. Place the volts/division setting of both channels on the same setting, making sure the zero reference line for both channels is the same.

Place the mode select switch in the add mode and invert.

Determine the voltage being displayed (V_{R_2}) and record this value in Table 33-2.

6. State the steps necessary to measure the voltage across R_1, using the subtract or (2-1) function of the oscilloscope.

At what point is the probe for the non-inverted channel placed to measure V_{R_1}?

At what point is the probe for the inverted channel placed to measure V_{R_1}?

Use the steps you wrote to measure the voltage across R_1, using the subtract function of the oscilloscope.

$V_{R_1} = $ _____ volts peak-to-peak

7. Subtract the voltage measured in Step 4 from the applied voltage.

_____ volts peak-to-peak

How does this value compare to the measured value in Step 6?

Record the value in Table 33-2.

8. Disconnect the oscilloscope from the circuit.

Using the DMM, measure the ac voltage across each resistor and record the value in Table 33-3.

Change the measured values in Table 33-2 to RMS values and record them in Table 33-3.

COMPONENT	OSCILLOSCOPE	DMM MEASURED VALUES
R_1		
R_2		
R_3		

Table 33-3

9. State your observations about the differences between the DMM measured values and the oscilloscope measured values that are converted in reference to the calculated values in Table 33-1. State which device, oscilloscope or DMM, is more accurate at higher frequencies. Are they both accurate?

10. Disconnect the DMM from the circuit and connect the oscilloscope probe of Channel 1 to measure the voltage across R_3.

   Slowly adjust the frequency control of the function generator, changing the frequency from greater than 10 kHz to less than 10 kHz. State your observations about the voltage amplitude across the resistor versus the change in frequency.

11. Adjust the frequency control of the function generator for 15 kHz.

   When the time/division setting of the oscilloscope is 10 μsec, how many divisions are in one complete cycle?

12. Connect Channel 1 of the oscilloscope to Point B.

   Disconnect both of the oscilloscope **ground leads** from the circuit, leaving the Channel 2 probe at Point C and the Channel 1 probe at Point B.

   State your observations.

Observations

1. Connect the ground lead of Channel 1 to Point C and state your observations about the voltage drop across R_3.

2. How many earth grounds or common reference points are there in the circuit with the ground lead of Channel 1 connected to Point C?

3. With this configuration, could the voltage drop across R_2 be measured accurately?

4. With this configuration, determine the sum of the voltage drops across R_2 and R_1.

Switches and Optoelectronics

Name_____ Class_____ Date_____

Objectives   Upon completion of this experiment, you should be able to:

- Observe the difference between a SPST (single-pole single-throw) switch and a SPDT (single-pole double-throw) switch.

- Connect a LED (light emitting diode) as an indicator.

Text   Terrell, *Fundamentals of Electronics: DC/AC Circuits*
Reference   Chapter 2, Sections 8 and 10.3

Materials   Fixed 5-volt or variable power supply; 0 to 20 volts dc
Required   Red LED @ 20 mA
Green LED @ 20 mA
180-Ω resistor
Voltmeter
Current meter
SPST switch
SPDT switch
Various test leads

Introduction

An LED (light emitting diode) is sometimes used as an **ON/OFF** indicator for some electronic equipment. The power supply is one type of equipment and the oscilloscope might be another type of equipment which would use the LED as an indicator.

Two basic types of switches are SPST (single-pole single-throw) and a SPDT (single-pole double-throw). Most other switches are variations of these basic types. The SPST has a single connection and is either open or closed. The SPDT has a single connection (the pole) that can be connected to one of two places.

The schematic representations for the two switches are shown in Figure 34-1. Figure 34-1A is a SPST, an open or closed switch.

Figure 34-1B, is a SPDT switch. Notice that the switch can be at either Position A or Position B, which allows one of two connections to occur.

Figure 34-1A   **Figure 34-1B**

Procedures

1. Construct the circuit shown in Figure 34-2.

   Observe the base of the body of the LED. Notice that one side of the base has a flat side; this is the cathode side of the LED. Connect the cathode side of the LED to the switch and the anode side (without the flat side on the base) to the resistor.

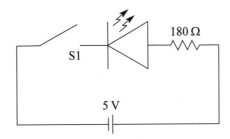

Figure 34-2

The cathode end of the LED is the straight line and is connected to the negative side of the voltage source through the switch. The anode is the arrow and is connected to the positive side of the voltage source through the resistor. The cathode end will have a straight side at the base of the LED.

With the switch open no current will flow through the LED. Once the switch is closed current will flow against the arrow.

2. Close the switch.

Discussion   The red LED should be illuminated when the switch is closed. If it does not come on, try reversing the LED. The SPST switch either makes a connection to turn on the LED or it does not.

---

3. Construct the circuit shown in Figure 34-3.

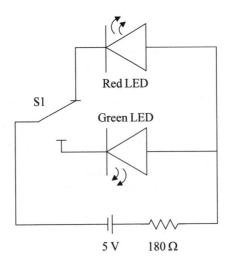

Figure 34-3

Discussion Notice this time that one of the LEDs is on all the time. If the SPDT switch is changed, the other LED will turn on. This indicates that either one connection is made or the other connection is made.

Observations

1. The 180-Ω resistor in Figure 34-2 is used to limit the current and drop the voltage not needed by the LED from the 5-volt power supply. Determine the current flowing through the LED.

2. Determine resistor size that would be needed if a 9-volt battery is used to power the LED. Use the same current value as determined in Observation 1.

3. Draw the schematic diagram, showing the size resistor needed. Then construct the circuit.

Magnetic Devices: DPDT Relay

Name_____ Class_____ Date _____

Objective Upon completion of this experiment, you should be able to:

- Observe the operation of a relay or solenoid that acts as a SPDT switch and a DPDT switch.

Text Reference Terrell, *Fundamentals of Electronics: DC/AC Circuits*
   Chapter 10, Sections 10-5.5, 10-5.6 and 10-6

Materials Required Ohmmeter
   Voltmeter
   Current meter
   Fixed 5-volt or dual variable power supply; 0 to 20 volts dc
   12-volt DPDT relay
   3-volt DPDT relay
   180-Ω resistor (1)
   47-Ω resistor, one-half Watt (1)
   SPST switch
   Various test leads
   1N914 or 1N4148 small signal diode

Introduction

Sometimes it is necessary to use switches that switch faster than can be done manually. Relays are used to switch at relatively fast speeds. They are also used to control large currents with a small switching current.

The relay used in this project is a double-pole double-throw (DPDT) relay, meaning that the relay will act as two single-pole double-throw (SPDT) switches.

The first step will be to discover how the relay is constructed, what pins are the normally closed contacts (NC), and what pins are the normally open contacts (NO). When no power is supplied to the relay, it is in its normal state. When power is supplied, the normally closed contacts open and the normally open contacts close. Observe Figure 35-2. The coil itself will have some dc resistance, usually less than 100 ohms. The normally closed contacts will have zero ohms and the normally open contacts will have infinite ohms.

Procedures

1. If the relay is turned upside down with the pins pointing up, the pin-out could look like the one shown in Figure 35-1. If the pin configuration is as shown, use the pin numbers indicated. If not, then the following information will help determine what normally open and closed contact pin numbers and the relay coil pin numbers are.

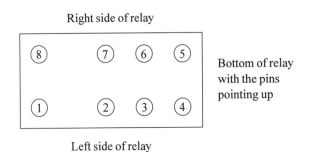

Right side of relay

Bottom of relay
with the pins
pointing up

Left side of relay

Figure 35-1

Pins 1 and 8 should be the pins used to connect the coil of the relay. The ohmmeter should read between 75 ohms and 200 ohms across the two pins.

Pins 2 and 3 should be normally closed and Pins 2 and 4 should be normally open. Pins 7 and 6 should be normally closed and Pins 7 and 5 should be normally open.

Using the ohmmeter, determine the pin numbers for the normally open and closed contacts and coil and indicate them in the provided spaces on the schematic diagram, Figure 35-2.

Relay coil resistance _____ Ω

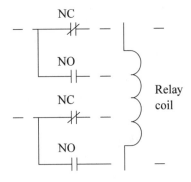

Figure 35-2

2. Using Figure 35-2 as a reference, connect the circuit shown in Figure 35-3.

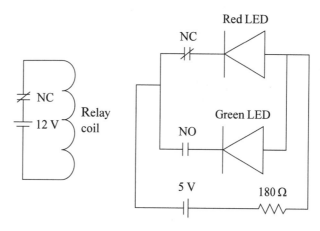

Figure 35-3

3. Adjust V1 to zero volts.

   Close S1. The red LED should be on.

   Slowly increase V1 until the green LED comes on.

   The relay will energize at _____ volts.

4. Open S1. The red LED should turn back on and the green LED should go off.

   Close S1. Slowly decrease V1, until the green LED goes off and the red LED turns on.

   The relay will de-energize at _____ volts.

   State your observations about the differences between the voltages that the relay energizes and de-energizes.

   Determine the current that each event occurs.

Discussion   The current level at which the relay energizes is referred to as the pick-up current; the current at which the relay de-energizes or drops out is referred to as drop-out current or holding current.

5. Construct the circuit shown in Figure 35-4. Note that the second pole of the relay is used in this circuit.

Discussion   The normally open contacts of the relay are in parallel with S1. The normally open contacts will close the instant S1 is closed; this allows the relay coil current to conduct through the contacts even if S1 is open. This circuit is referred to as a self-holding relay circuit. Switch S1 could be a momentary contact switch.

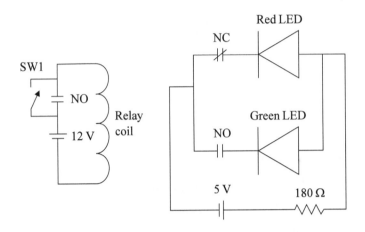

Figure 35-4

6. State your observations as you close S1, then open and close S1. Be sure to include the LEDs and the condition of the relay coil. (Energized or de-energized? What causes the relay to de-energize?)

7. Construct the circuit shown in Figure 35-5.

Discussion   This circuit is known as a chopper circuit. The relay will energize, and as soon as it does, the normally closed contacts will open, causing the relay to de-energize. As soon as it de-energizes the contacts close, causing the relay to energize again.

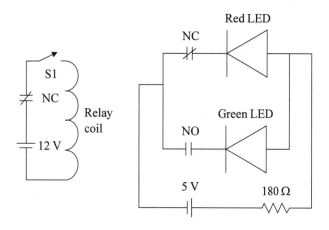

Figure 35-5

8. Close the switch and state your observations about the circuit and the noise factor. (Chattering relay)

9. Construct the circuit shown in Figure 35-6, using a 3-volt DPDT relay.

   Select the TTL output of the function generator. This output should be from a +5 volt- to zero-volt square wave.

   The 1N914 or 1N4148 is a small signal diode. The purpose of the diode will be examined in a later experiment.

   Adjust the frequency of the function generator for about 5 Hz.

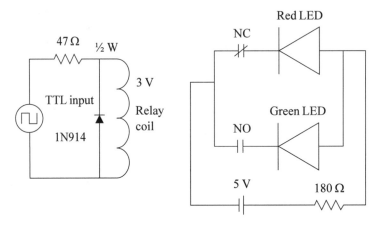

Figure 35-6

10. Increase and decrease the frequency of the function generator and state your observations about the frequency of the generator versus the flashing LEDs. (*Hint:* What value is the frequency before the LEDs appear not to flash or remain on all the time)?

Observations

1. Write at least three observations that you learned about using a relay, how fast lights can flash and be seen by the human eye, and relay switching speed versus manual switching speed.

Inductance: Level 1

Name_____ Class_____ Date _____

Objectives   Upon completion of this experiment, you should be able to:

- Observe the collasping magnetic field surrounding an inductor.

- Observe Faraday's Law.

- Observe the operation of a neon gas tube.

Text   Terrell, *Fundamentals of Electronics: DC/AC Circuits*
Reference   Chapter 10, Sections 10-2 and 10-3.1
            Chapter 12, Sections 12-1, 12-2.2, and 12-2.4

Materials   Variable power supply; 0 to 20 volts dc
Required   4 to 7 Henry inductor
        SPST switch
        NE2—neon gas tube
        12-volt DPDT relay
        Various test leads

Introduction

Faraday's Law simply states that as the number of lines of flux cuts across a coiled wire in a specified time, an induced voltage will result. If the specified time is decreased or if the number of flux lines increases for a given coil of wire, the induced voltage will increase.

In this experiment, a number of lines of flux will be generated around a coil of wire, by passing a dc current through the coil of wire. An induced voltage, larger than the applied, will be generated when the lines of flux rapidly collapse around the coil. The induced voltage will be large enough to cause a neon tube (NE2) to momentarily illuminate.

The collapsing field will generate an induced voltage in excess of 75 volts—the approximate voltage required to ionize the neon gas inside the NE2.

Procedures

1. Construct the circuit shown in Figure 36-1.

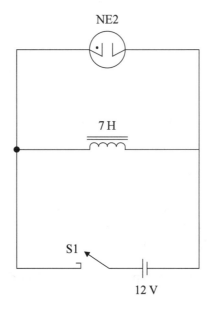

Figure 36-1

2. Close switch S1, count to ten.

   Open switch S1.

   State your observations, remembering it takes 70 to 75 volts to turn on the NE2.

   With 12 volts dc applied, the voltage to illuminate the NE2 was generated by:

   What Law was observed?

3. Construct the circuit shown in Figure 36-2.

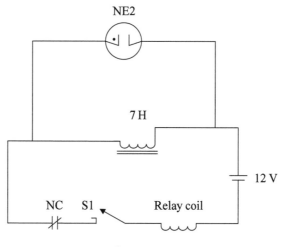

Figure 36-2

4. Close switch S1 and state your observation concerning the NE2 illumination.

Inductance: Level II

Name_____ Class_____ Date_____

Objectives Upon completion of this experiment, you should be able to:

- Observe the difference in voltage drops across different inductor values.

- Measure voltages across ungrounded components, using the subtract function of the oscilloscope.

*Text
Reference* Terrell, *Fundamentals of Electronics: DC/AC Circuits*
    Chapter 10, Section 10-3.1
    Chapter 12, Sections 12-1.4, 12-2.3, and 12-4.1

*Materials
Required* Dual time-base oscilloscope
Function generator (sine wave generator)
1-mH inductor
10-mH inductor
100-mH inductor
Various leads

Introduction

In the previous experiment, a switch was used to create a change in current that caused the inductor to oppose the change. The inductor stored energy in the form of a magnetic field when the switch was closed. When the switch opened the magnetic field collapsed. The inductor takes energy from the circuit to oppose an increase in current and puts energy back into the circuit, opposing a decrease in current. In an ac circuit the current is constantly changing. Therefore, the opposition to the change in current is directly proportional to the size of the inductor. The larger the inductor, the greater the opposition to the change in current; this causes a larger induced voltage across the inductor.

Learning to use the oscilloscope to measure voltages across ungrounded components is very important in troubleshooting. In this experiment, several voltages will be measured using the subtract function of the oscilloscope. The triggering function of the oscilloscope will also be a point of emphasis. This function will become more important in future experiments.

Procedures

1. Construct the circuit shown in Figure 37-1.

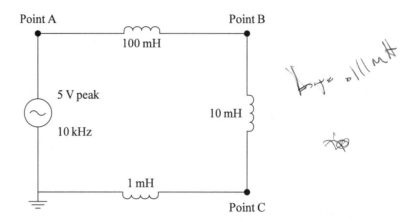

Figure 37-1

> **Note** Remember that the generator ground lead is earth ground and that all oscilloscope leads are automatically connected to this point.

2. Set the oscilloscope controls as follows:

   Triggering source . . . .   Channel 2

   Time/division . . . .   10 μ sec./division

   Volts/division . . . .   2 volts/division

   Mode select . . . .   dual

   Slope . . . .   (+)

   Set the zero reference line in the center for both channels.

3. Using Channel 2, measure the voltage at Point A and adjust the triggering level so that the waveform starts at 0°, or just starts going positive at the center of the screen on the far left-hand side. Once the triggering level is set, do not adjust unless absolutely necessary. Adjust the vertical position control and horizontal position control until the start of the trace is in the left-hand corner of the center of the screen. This will be referred to as the **standard position** from this point forward. Observe Figure 37-2.

Discussion   One complete cycle should now be displayed, covering 2.5 divisions vertically and 10 divisions horizontally.

At any time necessary adjust the volts/division setting or the time/division setting of the oscilloscope to make it easier to measure the voltage amplitudes. The horizontal position control will also assist in measuring voltage amplitudes. Remember, when using the subtract function of the oscilloscope, the volts/division setting of both channels must be the same.

For the purposes of this and future experiments, the channel that can be inverted will be referred to as Channel 1 and the channel that cannot be inverted will be referred to as Channel 2.

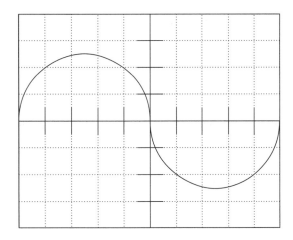

Figure 37-2

4. Place the oscilloscope controls to:

   Mode select . . . .   add (or subtract)

   Invert Channel 1

5. Connect Channel 2 at Point C and Channel 1 at ground. Think of Channel 2 as the red lead of a meter and Channel 1 as the ground or common lead of a meter.

   The voltage being measured is the voltage across the 1 mH inductor.

   $V_{1\,mH}$ = __50m__ v pk

6. Connect Channel 2 at Point B and Channel 1 at Point C.

   $V_{10\,mH}$ = __.5__ v pk

7. Connect Channel 2 at Point A and Channel 1 at Point B.

   $V_{100\,mH}$ = ~~5~~ 4.5 v pk

8. Using the information obtained in Steps 5, 6, and 7 answer the following questions.

   Which inductor offered the highest opposition to the change in current?

   The 100 mH inductor

   Which inductor, if removed from the circuit, would cause only a slight increase in voltage across the remaining inductors?

   The 1mH inductor

   Which inductor, if removed from the circuit, would cause the largest increase in voltage across the remaining inductors?

   The 100 mH inductor

Discussion   The larger value inductor will offer the largest amount of opposition; it has the largest voltage drop. If the smallest inductor were removed, only a small increase in voltage would occur. If the largest value inductor were removed a large increase in voltage would be noted.

---

9. Prove these answers by removing the 1-mH inductor. (Place a jumper wire in its place.)

$V_{10\ mH}$ = _____.505_____ v pk

$V_{100\ mH}$ = _____4.565_____ v pk

Remove the jumper wire and replace the 1-mH inductor.

Remove the 100-mH inductor and place a jumper wire in its place.

$V_{1\ mH}$ = _____.46 M_____ v pk

$V_{10\ mH}$ = _____4.75_____ v pk

Observations

1. State your observations about the value of the inductor versus the voltage drop across the inductor and how to determine which inductor is shorted, by measuring the voltage across all three inductors.

Inductance: Level III

Name_____ Class_____ Date _____

Objectives Upon completion of this experiment, you should be able to:

- Observe the phase shift between circuit current and voltage across the inductor in an series AC RL circuit.

- Observe the phase shift between the applied voltage and circuit current in an series AC RL circuit.

- Draw waveforms and time relationship graphs on linear graph paper.

- Use the external trigger control of the oscilloscope.

Text Reference Terrell, *Fundamentals of Electronics: DC/AC Circuits*
Chapter 11, Section 11-6
Chapter 12, Section 12-6
Chapter 13, Section 13-1

Materials Required Function generator (sine wave)
100-mH inductor
3.3-kΩ resistor
Linear graph paper
Various test leads

Introduction

Because the inductor opposes a change in current, the current will lag behind the voltage across the inductor. This, in turn, causes the applied voltage to lead the circuit current in a series resistive-inductive circuit.

In this experiment waveform time-relationship graphs will be drawn to represent the waveforms across each circuit component. In order to show time-relationship graphs, a reference must be established for time. The applied voltage will be used in this experiment as a time reference to draw the graphs and for the oscilloscope. See Sample Graph for reference, Figure 38-4.

The external trigger input will be connected across the input voltage. This will set the time reference to a constant point. It is important to note: **Once the time reference is set, the triggering level must NOT be adjusted, or the time reference will change.**

This experiment will measure the phase shift between two waveforms of the same frequency. The procedures outlined will be used in future experiments without listing the actual steps.

Procedures

1. Construct the circuit shown in Figure 38-1.

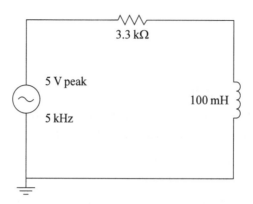

Figure 38-1

2. Connect the external trigger input across the input voltage. Connect Channel 2 to measure the input voltage and adjust the oscilloscope controls until the waveform is in the **standard position.** (Refer to Experiment 37 if in doubt.)

   Note   Remember **Do Not** adjust the triggering level after this step is completed.

   Adjust the time/division setting of the oscilloscope one position CW.

   Adjust the calibrate control of the time/division selector switch until one complete cycle is nine horizontal divisions. Refer to Figure 38-2.

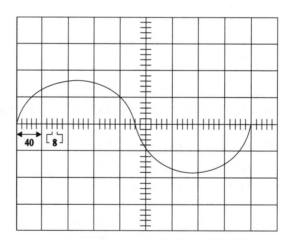

Figure 38-2

Discussion   If one complete cycle is nine (9) divisions, then each division represents 40°.

$$\frac{360°}{9} = 40°$$

Also note that each division has 5 smaller increments.

$$\frac{40°}{5} = 8°$$

Nine divisions per complete cycle was picked because the smaller increments came out a whole number. If desired, other divisions per complete cycle can be used.

Example   10 divisions per complete cycle: 36° per division; 7.2° per small increment.

---

3. Adjust the horizontal position control of the oscilloscope until the point that represents 180° on the sine wave is in the exact center of the screen. This will be a point of reference.

4. Connect Channel 1 to measure the voltage across the inductor, placing the mode select control of the oscilloscope at **dual**.

Discussion   Note that the reference waveform has not moved and that the voltage waveform across the inductor does not coincide with the reference waveform, in time relationship.

Note where the Channel 1 waveform crosses the X-axis at 180°. (The part of the waveform that just starts to go negative.)

---

5. Count the number of divisions between where Channel 2 is at 180° and Channel 1 is at 180°.

Number of divisions _____

Your answer should be around 1 to 1.2 divisions.

Multiply the number of divisions by 40° (degrees per division). This will indicate the phase difference between the two waveforms. The phase shift should be around 40° to 50°.

Discussion   Notice that Channel 1 gets to 180° before Channel 2 gets to 180°. This indicates that Channel 1 is **leading** Channel 2 by the degrees indicated in the above step or Channel 2 **lags** Channel 1 by the number of degrees determined in the above step. Refer to Figure 38-3 for reference.

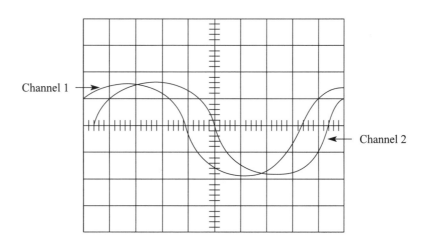

Figure 38-3

6. Measure the voltage amplitude across the inductor.

   $V_{100\,mH}$ = _____ v pk

7. Set the volts/division setting of both channels to the same setting.

   Change the mode select control to **add,** or the subtract function, and invert Channel 1.

   Remembering that the time reference signal is at 180°, in the exact center of the screen. Determine where the voltage waveform crosses the X-axis at 180°.

   Count the number of divisions difference and multiply by 40°. This indicates the phase shift between the voltage across the resistor and the applied voltage.

   Phase shift in degrees _____

Discussion   Remember from previous experiments that the resistor does not create a phase shift. Therefore, the current through the resistor and the voltage across the resistor are in-phase. The waveform is a representation of the total circuit current in a series resistive-inductive circuit.

   This time, the waveform represented is **lagging** the applied voltage by approximately 45°, or the applied voltage is leading the resistor voltage drop.

   If the two phase shift angles are added together, they should equal approximately 90°. This indicates that the voltage across the inductor (Channel 1) is leading the total circuit current (resistor voltage) by 90°. Therefore, the applied voltage is lagging the inductor voltage and leading the total circuit current.

---

8. Measure the voltage across the resistor.

   V_R = _____ v pk

   Compare this value to the inductor voltage and state your observations.

9. Using linear graph paper, draw the applied voltage inductor and resistor voltage waveforms. Be sure to accurately indicate the timing relationship by showing the phase relationship; also indicate the voltage amplitudes for each waveform. The applied voltage should be shown in the **standard position** at the top of the graph. See Sample Graph, Figure 38-4.

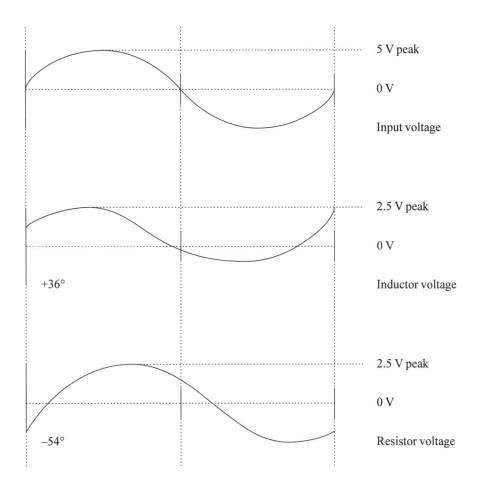

Figure 38-4

Capacitors: Level I

Name_____ Class_____ Date _____

Objectives   Upon completion of this experiment, you should be able to:

- Observe that the size of the capacitor determines the value of voltage across the capacitor in a dc and ac circuit.

- Observe the stored charge in a capacitor.

Text Reference   Terrell, *Fundamentals of Electronics: DC/AC Circuits*
        Chapter 14, Sections 14-1, 14-3, and 14-6

Materials Required   Variable power supply; 0 to 20 volts dc
    Function generator (sine wave)
    Ohmmeter
    Voltmeter (DMM or very high impedance voltmeter; FET-meter)
    Dual-trace oscilloscope
    1000-µF capacitor
    100-µF capacitor
    0.1-µF capacitor
    0.022-µF capacitor
    0.01-µF capacitor
    SPDT switch
    Various test leads

Introduction

The inductor stores energy in the form of a magnetic field, whereas the capacitor stores energy in the form of a electrostatic field. The larger the capacitor, the more energy or charge (Q; coulombs) that can be stored.

A low impedance voltmeter placed in parallel with a capacitor will cause the capacitor voltage to **discharge** through the voltmeter. When measuring the voltage across the capacitor, a high impedance voltmeter is required. Remember that the DMM has 10 MΩ of impedance, whereas the VOM has 20 kΩ per volt of impedance.

When checking a capacitor with an ohmmeter, the size of the capacitor will determine if it is a valid check for an open capacitor. If the capacitor is large, it can be checked with a ohmmeter. However, if the capacitor is small, an ohmmeter is not necessarily a valid check.

Procedures

1. Construct the circuit shown in Figure 40-1, using a 1000-μ farad capacitor for C_1.

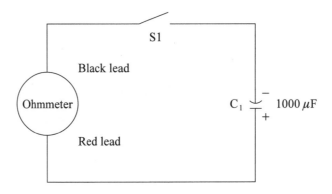

Figure 40-1

2. Close switch S1 and state your observations.

3. Open switch S1 and replace C_1 with a 100-μ farad capacitor. Close switch S1 and state your observations; include differences between what you observed in Step 2 and the observations for this step.

4. Open switch S1 and replace C_1 with a 0.01-μ farad capacitor. State your observations.

Discussion   When you used the 1000 μF capacitor the ohmic value was very low and then **slowly** changed to a very high value. The smaller the capacitor, the less time it takes to reach the high value indication on the ohmmeter.

---

5. Construct the circuit shown in Figure 40-2.

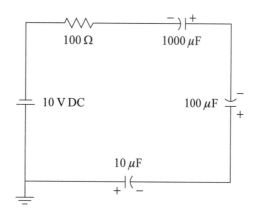

Figure 40-2

6. Using a high impedance dc voltmeter, measure the voltage across each capacitor, following each step carefully. Record indications in Table 40-1.

> ⚡**CAUTION** Each capacitor must be measured using the following procedures. Be sure to start at the beginning (a.) for each capacitor.

a. **Turn off the power supply.**

b. With a jumper wire, short across each capacitor and then remove the jumper wire.

c. Turn on the power supply.

d. Place the voltmeter across the capacitor to be measured and record the voltage that is indicated at the **first** instant an indication occurs on the voltmeter. Record the **highest** reading in Table 40-1.

CAPACITOR	CAPACITOR VOLTAGE
1000 µF	
100 µF	
10 µF	

Table 40-1

7. Construct the circuit shown in Figure 40-3.

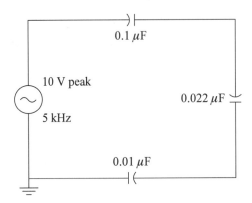

Figure 40-3

8. Using the subtract function of the oscilloscope, measure the peak voltage across each capacitor in Figure 40-3 and record the voltage value in Table 40-2.

CAPACITOR	CAPACITOR VOLTAGE
0.1 µF	
0.022 µF	
0.01 µF	

Table 40-2

Observations

Answer the following questions using your observations, Figures 40-1 and 40-2, and Tables 40-1 and 40-2 as references.

1. Did the 0.01-µ farad capacitor appear open when measuring with the ohmmeter?

2. For small value capacitors, is an ohmmeter check a **good** indication of a capacitor?

3. Look at Figure 40-2 and Figure 40-3. Which capacitor has the largest measured voltage? Is it the smallest or largest capacitor?

4. Did the sum of the voltages across the capacitors in Figures 40-2 and 40-3, approximately equal the applied voltage?

5. In Figures 40-2 and 40-3 which capacitor has the largest charge (Q or coulombs)? (*Hint:* Q = VC)

6. Describe the purpose of R_1, in Figure 40-2?

7. How much voltage is across R_1, in Figure 40-2?

8. Explain the voltage indication across R_1 in Figure 40-2.

9. In Figure 40-3, are all of the voltage waveforms in-phase with the applied voltage?

Discussion   The smallest capacitor should have had the largest voltage drop. The sum of the voltages across the capacitors should have been approximately equal to the applied voltage, but each voltage should have been close to −90° out-of-phase with the applied voltage.

Capacitors: Level II

Name _____ Class _____ Date _____

Objectives   Upon completion of this experiment, you should be able to:

- Observe the phase angle between the applied voltage and resistor voltage, the applied voltage and capacitor voltage, and the applied voltage and total circuit current.

- Determine by experimentation the total circuit current, any relevant phase angle, the capacitor voltage, and the resistor voltage.

- Draw the voltage waveforms showing time relationships and draw phasor diagrams representing the time relationship waveforms.

Text Reference   Terrell, *Fundamentals of Electronics: DC/AC Circuits*
    Chapter 14, Section 14-4
    Chapter 15, Sections 15-1 and 15-3

Materials Required   Function generator (sine wave)
    Dual-trace oscilloscope
    1-kΩ resistor
    0.033-µF capacitor
    Various test leads

Introduction

The same basic concepts used to analyze ac inductive-resistive circuits can be used to analyze ac capacitive-resistive circuits. However, in AC RL circuits, the inductor voltage leads the applied voltage and the applied voltage leads the resistor voltage. In AC RC circuits, the resistor voltage leads the applied voltage and the applied voltage leads the capacitor voltage.

Remember that the voltage across the resistor and the circuit current are always in-phase. The same value of current that flows through the resistor will also determine the value of voltage across the capacitor.

The capacitive reactance value and the resistance value will determine the total circuit impedance, which, along with the applied voltage, determines the total circuit current.

When drawing the time relationship waveforms, use the applied voltage as the reference (triggering source) and show the phase angle between all three waveforms. The resistor voltage represents the total circuit current waveform (phase angle).These waveforms can be used to show the relationship of the phasor or vector diagram.

Procedures

1. Measure the actual value of the 1-kΩ resistor.

   Resistor value _977_ Ω

2. Construct the circuit shown in Figure 41-1.

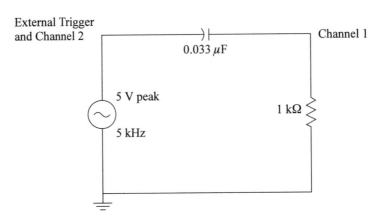

Figure 41-1

3. Use the oscilloscope to measure the peak voltage drop across the 1-kΩ resistor.

   V_R pk = _5V_

4. Determine the reactance of the capacitor (X_C) by using the equation:

$$\frac{1}{2\pi C f} = X_C$$

   $X_c = 909 \, \Omega$

5. Determine the total circuit current by dividing the resistor voltage by the actual measured value of resistor.

   Total circuit current _5_ mA pk

6. Determine the peak capacitor voltage by multiplying the total circuit current by the calculated X_C value.

   V_{XC} pk = _4.5 Volts_

7. Using the subtract function of the oscilloscope, measure the voltage across the capacitor.

V_{XC} pk = _~~5.2V~~_ *(handwritten: 5.2V)*

State your observations about the variance between the value calculated and the measured value.

Variance is caused by approximation & pure math values are subject to have little variances

8. Using the voltage measured in Step 7 and the calculated total circuit current, determine the X_C value, where:

$$X_C = \frac{V_{XC}}{I_{Total}}$$

$X_C = 1.04 \ K\angle\Omega$

9. Determine the actual capacitance value by using:

35pF

$$\frac{0.15923}{X_c f} = C \quad \text{where } 0.15923 = \frac{1}{2\pi}$$

State your observations about the stated value versus the actual value of capacitance. If a capacitance meter is available, measure the capacitance value with the meter.

Stated values & measured values will differ a little due to approximations &/or assumptions

10. Connect the oscilloscope external trigger across the applied voltage and select the **EXT** triggering mode. Measure the voltage across the resistor and determine the phase angle between the applied voltage and the resistor voltage.

    Phase angle *46.12*°

    Using the subtract function of the oscilloscope, measure the voltage across the capacitor and determine the phase angle between the applied voltage and the capacitor voltage.

    Phase angle *43.88*   *5.1*

11. What is the sum of the two phase angles?

    Is 90°

    By what quadrant of the X-Y axis would the phasor diagram be represented?

    The 4th quadrant

Discussion   The sum of the phase angles should be close to 90°, with the resistor voltage leading the applied voltage and the capacitor voltage lagging the applied voltage. Remember that the resistor voltage represents the total circuit current phase angle. The fourth quadrant would be represented by the phasor diagram.

---

12. Using the supplied X-Y axis, draw the phasor diagram and indicate the measured phase angles. Indicate the peak voltage amplitudes.

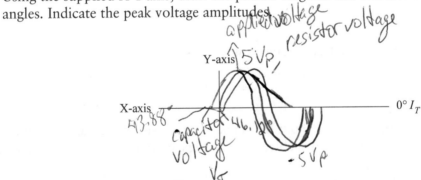

Figure 41-2

13. Using linear graph paper, draw the time relationship waveforms. Indicate the time relationship between the applied voltage and all other voltage waveforms, peak amplitudes, phase angles, and the dc voltage references.

Observations

1. Add the peak values of the resistor and capacitor and state your observations.

   Resistor Peak Voltage leads the applied voltage
   Capacitor Peak Voltage lags applied voltage.
   Both voltages when combined

2. Using the time relationship graph, draw a vertical line that intersects all three waveforms when the applied voltage is at 90°.

   Determine the voltage of each waveform at the point where the line intersects the waveforms.

   $V_{applied}$ = _____5_____ volts

   V_R = _____3.5_____ volts

   V_{XC} = _____1.5_____ volts

3. Add the instantaneous capacitor and resistor voltage values and state your observations.

   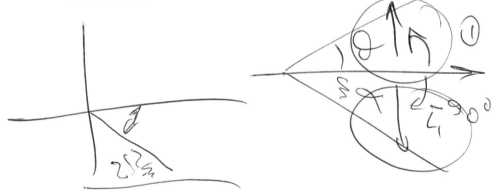

4. If the applied voltage is at 120°, determine the angle for the resistor voltage and the capacitor voltage at this same time. Use the time relationship graph.

   The applied voltage is at 120°

   The resistor voltage is at _____120_____ °

   The capacitor voltage is at _____210_____ °

5. Find the instantaneous value of voltage for each sine wave.

   $$v_{inst.} = sine\ \theta\ V_{pk}$$

   $V_{inst.\ applied}$ = _____5 V_____

   $V_{inst.\ resistor}$ = _____3.6 V_____

   $V_{inst.\ capacitor}$ = _____3.46 V_____

6. Add the instantaneous values of the resistor and capacitor together and state your observations. Does Kirchhoff's Voltage Law still apply to ac circuits?

Capacitors: Level III

Name_____ Class_____ Date _____

Objectives   Upon completion of this experiment, you should be able to:

- Observe changes in voltage amplitudes and phase angles as the input frequency is varied.

- Observe changes in voltage amplitudes and phase angles as the resistance is varied.

- Draw a functional graph, for analysis, of frequency versus voltage amplitudes.

Text   Terrell, *Fundamentals of Electronics: DC/AC Circuits*
Reference   Chapter 14, Section 14-4.1
             Chapter 15, Sections 15-1, 15-3.1, and 15-5.2

Materials   Function generator (sine wave)
Required   Dual-trace oscilloscope
          0.1-μF capacitor
          0.01-μF capacitor
          0.001-μF capacitor
          10-kΩ variable resistor
          Various test leads

Introduction

Variations in the voltage amplitudes can be observed by varying the input voltage amplitude, frequency, the resistor, and the capacitance value. As frequency is varied, the reactance of the capacitor changes causing a change in voltage amplitudes across the resistor and capacitor. The phase angle between the capacitor and the applied voltage will also change as the frequency is changed.

In this experiment the resistor value and the frequency are changed to allow you to observe the changes that occur across the capacitor. At low frequencies the capacitive reactance is larger than the resistor; therefore, the voltage across the capacitor is larger than the voltage across the resistor. As the frequency is increased, the voltage across the capacitor decreases and the voltage across the resistor increases due to the decrease in the capacitive reactance value.

Procedures

1. Construct the circuit shown in Figure 42-1. Adjust the variable resistor to 3.2 kΩ.

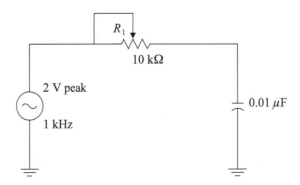

Figure 42-1

2. Lay out a sheet of linear graph paper (frequency 1 kHz to 10 kHz). The long side of the graph should be across the bottom (X-axis) and voltage, short side of the graph paper, along the left-hand side (Y-axis) from 0 volts to 2 volts peak.

3. Measure the peak voltage across the capacitor, at 1-kHz intervals, from 1 kHz to 10 kHz, making sure the applied voltage is maintained at 2 volts peak at each frequency.

   Plot each capacitor peak voltage on the graph.

4. Repeat Step 3, measuring the peak voltage across the resistor. Plot the resistor voltage on the same graph paper for comparison.

5. State your observations about the graphs, including the point at which the two graphs cross.

Discussion   The observations should include statements about the decreasing voltage amplitude of the capacitor and the increasing voltage amplitude of the resistor. The point at where the two graphs cross indicates that the voltages are equal. At this frequency the reactance value is equal to the resistance value.

---

6. While monitoring the capacitor voltage and the applied voltage, adjust the function generator frequency until the phase angle between the applied voltage and capacitor voltage is at 45°.

   At what frequency does this occur? _____ Hz

   Does this approximately match the frequency indicated by the graph where the resistor voltage and the capacitor voltage are the same? Is it very close?

7. While monitoring the phase angle between the capacitor voltage and the applied voltage, slowly vary the frequency down to 1 kHz and state your observations.

8. Slowly vary the frequency of the generator to 10 kHz, again monitoring the capacitor voltage and the applied voltage phase angle. State your observations.

Discussion   As the generator was varied down toward 1 kHz the voltage across the capacitor should have increased and the phase angle should have decreased. As the voltage was varied up to 10 kHz, the voltage across the capacitor should have decreased and the phase angle increased. Observing the graph for the capacitor should confirm your observations.

---

9. Adjust the generator to a frequency where the applied voltage and the capacitor voltage are 45° out-of-phase.

   Slowly vary the rheostat until the capacitor voltage and the applied voltage appear to be in-phase. Is the resistance value at maximum or minimum?

State the steps used to prove your answer. (*Hint:* Ohmmeter)

10. Slowly vary the rheostat until the capacitor voltage and the applied voltage appear to be 90° out-of-phase or as far out-of-phase as possible.

    Is the resistor value at maximum or minimum?

11. Readjust the variable resistor to 3.2 kΩ. Replace the 0.01-μF capacitor with a 0.1-μF capacitor.

12. Measure the voltage across the capacitor and the phase angle between the applied voltage and the capacitor voltage. State your observations about the changes that occurred in the voltage amplitude and the phase angle as compared to the 0.01 μF capacitor. Remember, the frequency was adjusted for a 45° phase angle with the 0.01-μF capacitor.

13. Replace the 0.1-μF capacitor with a 0.001-μF capacitor.

14. Measure the voltage across the capacitor and the phase angle between the applied voltage and the capacitor voltage.

    State your observations about the changes that occurred in the phase angle between the applied voltage and capacitor voltage, the phase angle between the applied voltage and total circuit current, and the component voltage amplitudes. The graph might be a helpful tool to use when you state your observations.

Observations

Using the graph and the observations, answer the following questions.

1. As the frequency is increased, what changed to cause a decrease in capacitor voltage and an increase in resistor voltage?

2. As the frequency is increased what happens to total circuit current?

3. What changed to indicate that the circuit current changed?

4. What is indicated at the point where the two graphs cross? (*Hint:* The graph indicates that the voltages are equal and Figure 42-1 is a series circuit.)

5. Could the actual capacitance value be determined, using the value of the resistor in Figure 42-1 and the graphs?

Explain by determining the actual capacitance value (Show work.)

Capacitors: RC Time Constant; Level IV

Name_____ Class_____ Date _____

Objectives	Upon completion of this experiment, you should be able to:

- Observe the impedance of the DMM when measuring DC voltages.
- Observe the charge and discharge time of a capacitor.
- Draw a time constant charge/discharge curve.

***Text
Reference***   Terrell, *Fundamentals of Electronics: DC/AC Circuits*
    Chapter 15, Section 15-4

***Materials
Required***   Variable power supply; 0 to 20 volts dc
DMM or high impedance voltmeter
SPDT switch (use as an SPST switch)
2-MΩ resistor
10-μF capacitor
2.2-μF capacitor
0.0033-μF capacitor
Linear graph paper
Some device for measuring seconds

Introduction

In order to create a long RC time constant, a large resistance and capacitor must be used. The DMM has a large resistance, around 10 megaohms (10 MΩ). This experiment will show how to measure the input impedance of the DMM or other devices.

Refer to Figure 43-1 for the purposes of this discussion. The DMM will act as the series resistance and will also indicate the voltage across itself. If the actual value of the 2-MΩ resistor is known, then the DMM resistance can be determined by using the equation:

$$\frac{voltage\ DMM}{voltage\ 2\ M\Omega} = \frac{resistance\ DMM}{resistance\ 2\ M\Omega}$$

The voltage across the DMM is known as well as the applied voltage. Therefore, the voltage across the 2-MΩ resistor can be determined. The only unknown is the impedance (resistance) of the DMM.

The next part of the experiment will require at least two persons. One person to monitor time and the second person to monitor the voltage indications at given time intervals.

The RC time constant for the experiment should be 22 seconds. If the impedance (resistance) of the DMM is not at least 10 MΩ, adjust the capacitor size to a larger value. Get as close to 22 seconds as possible. If the impedance (resistance) of the DMM is greater than 10 MΩ, **do not** adjust the size of the capacitor.

Procedures

1. Measure the actual value of the 2-MΩ resistor. The 20-Megaohm range of the DMM may be required to accurately measure the resistor.

   Actual resistance _____ Ω

   Actual power supply setting _____ volts (Figure 43-1)

2. Construct the circuit shown in Figure 43-1, setting DMM #1 controls to measure 10 volts dc.

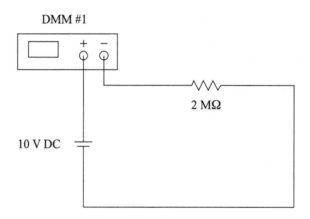

Figure 43-1

3. Using the DMM indication and the power supply setting recorded in Step 1, determine the voltage across the 2-MΩ resistor.

   $V_{2\,M\Omega}$ = _____

4. Using the equation in the Introduction, determine the impedance (resistance) of the DMM.

   R_{DMM} = _____

5. If a capacitance meter is available, measure the actual value of the 2.2-μF capacitor. If not, use the stated value.

   C_1 value used _____ μF

6. Determine the RC time constant (τ), using the determined value of the DMM and recorded value of the capacitor.

   τ = _____ seconds

7. Construct the circuit shown in Figure 43-2.

Do not close S1 until instructed. If the switch is inadvertently closed or the timing process needs to be restarted, short across the capacitor with a jumper wire, with switch S1 **open**, then restart the timing process.

The instant switch S1 is closed, start the timing process. Record the voltage across the DMM at the times indicated in Table 43-1.

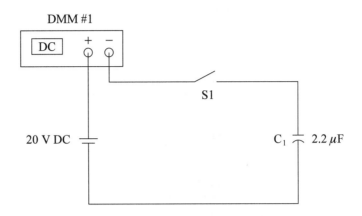

Figure 43-2

TIME	DMM VOLTAGE
10 SEC.	
20 SEC.	
30 SEC.	
40 SEC.	
50 SEC.	
60 SEC.	
70 SEC.	
80 SEC.	
90 SEC.	
100 SEC.	
110 SEC.	
120 SEC.	
130 SEC.	

Table 43-1

8. Using Table 43-2, determine the capacitor voltage by subtracting the DMM voltage from the power supply voltage.

TIME	CAPACITOR VOLTAGE
10 SEC.	
20 SEC.	
30 SEC.	
40 SEC.	
50 SEC.	
60 SEC.	
70 SEC.	
80 SEC.	
90 SEC.	
100 SEC.	
110 SEC.	
120 SEC.	
130 SEC.	

Table 43-2

9. Using linear graph paper, plot each capacitor voltage (Y-axis, short side) versus time (X-axis, long side).

10. Using the RC time constant recorded in Step 6, draw a vertical line at each RC time constant interval (1τ, 2τ, 3τ, 4τ, and 5τ).

11. List the capacitor voltage value at each of the time intervals.

1τ _____ volts

2τ _____ volts

3τ _____ volts

4τ _____ volts

5τ _____ volts

12. Using the values in Step 11, determine the percentage of the applied voltage that is across the capacitor at each time interval.

$$\frac{capacitor\ voltage}{power\ supply\ voltage} \times 100 = \%\ of\ change\ across\ capacitor$$

% at 1τ = _____

% at 2τ = _____

% at 3τ = _____

% at 4τ = _____

% at 5τ = _____

13. Plot the DMM (resistor) voltage on the same graph (Table 43-1).

14. State your observations about the following values:

Time versus the capacitor voltage

Time versus the resistor voltage

Time versus the circuit current

15. Open switch S1 and replace the 2.2-μF capacitor with a 10-μF capacitor.

Using Table 43-3, record the DMM (resistor) voltage at the times indicated after switch S1 is closed.

TIME	DMM VOLTAGE	CAPACITOR VOLTAGE
10 SEC.		
20 SEC.		
30 SEC.		
40 SEC.		
50 SEC.		
60 SEC.		
70 SEC.		
80 SEC.		
90 SEC.		
100 SEC.		
110 SEC.		
120 SEC.		
130 SEC.		

Table 43-3

16. Determine the capacitor voltage at the indicated times and state your observations, comparing the voltage levels in Tables 43-1 and 43-2 to the voltage levels in Table 43-3. Also include the comparisons of resistor voltages and the circuit current at the different time intervals.

17. Open switch S1 and replace the 10-μF capacitor with a 0.0033-μF capacitor.

Using Table 43-4, record the DMM (resistor) voltage at the times indicated after switch S1 is closed.

TIME	DMM VOLTAGE	CAPACITOR VOLTAGE
10 SEC.		
20 SEC.		
30 SEC.		
40 SEC.		
50 SEC.		
60 SEC.		
70 SEC.		
80 SEC.		
90 SEC.		
100 SEC.		
110 SEC.		
120 SEC.		
130 SEC.		

Table 43-4

18. Determine the capacitor voltage at the indicated times and state your observations, comparing the voltage levels in Tables 43-1, 43-2, and 43-3 to the voltage levels in Table 43-4. Also include the comparisons of length of time to totally charge the capacitor.

19. Construct the circuit shown in Figure 43-3.

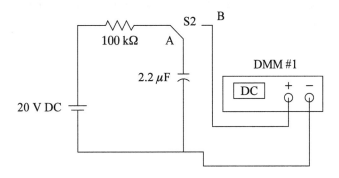

Figure 43-3

20. Leave switch S2 in Position A to allow the capacitor to fully charge. Change switch S2 to Position B and start timing the capacitor discharge, recording the DMM voltages at the indicated time intervals in Table 43-5.

   Note   If the timing sequence needs to be restarted, remember to fully charge the capacitor before placing S2 in Position B.

TIME	DMM VOLTAGE	CAPACITOR VOLTAGE
10 SEC.		
20 SEC.		
30 SEC.		
40 SEC.		
50 SEC.		
60 SEC.		
70 SEC.		
80 SEC.		
90 SEC.		
100 SEC.		
110 SEC.		
120 SEC.		
130 SEC.		

Table 43-5

21. Compare the discharge values to the values listed in Table 43-1 and state your observations.

Observations

1. Which capacitor took the longest to charge?

2. Using the RC time constant chart drawn in Step 9, determine the capacitor voltage at 1.5 time constants. Determine the percent change in voltage across the capacitor from the time the switch was closed in Figure 43-1 until 1.5 time constants have occurred.

3. Using the information from Table 43-3, determine the percent change in voltage across the capacitor after 1.5 time constants have occurred.

4. Using the information in Table 43-5, determine the percent change in voltage across the capacitor after 1.5 time constants have occurred.

5. State what has been noted by answering Observations 2, 3, and 4.

Capacitors: Coupling and Bypass; Level V

Name_____ Class_____ Date _____

Objectives   Upon completion of this experiment, you should be able to:

- Observe a sinusoidal waveform with a non-zero volt reference voltage.

- Observe the effects of coupling and bypass capacitors.

Text   Terrell, *Fundamentals of Electronics: DC/AC Circuits*
Reference   Chapter 18, Section 18-5
                   Chapter 15, Section 15-4

Materials   Dual-variable power supply; 0 to 20 volts dc
Required   Dual-trace oscillscope
           Function generator (sine wave)
           Voltmeter
           1-kΩ resistors (2)
           1.8-kΩ resistor
           2.2-kΩ resistor
           3.3-kΩ resistor
           4.7-kΩ resistor
           10-μF capacitors (2)
           Various test leads

Introduction

A sine wave is an unique waveform that has a zero-volt reference voltage. A sine wave that does not have a zero-volt reference voltage, but still looks and acts like a sine wave, is referred to as a sinusoidal waveform. An example of a sinusoidal waveform is shown in Figure 44-1.

Notice that the center reference voltage is 10 volts, the positive peak value is 11 volts, and the negative peak value is 9 volts. The peak-to-peak voltage is 2 volts. Without the 10-volt reference voltage, the peak value would be 1-volt peak. A coupling capacitor is sometimes used to remove the non-zero-volt reference voltage or to isolate one dc reference voltage from another dc reference voltage.

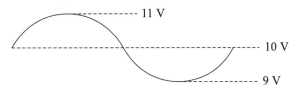

Figure 44-1

Coupling and bypass capacitors are special application filter circuits. A coupling capacitor is used to couple an ac signal from one ungrounded point to another ungrounded point in the circuit. This also allows for dc isolation between two dc voltage points, without effecting the dc voltage values or the ac voltage.

A bypass capacitor is designed to create a low impedance to the ac signal without changing the dc voltage at a specific point in a circuit. One side of a bypass capacitor is often at ground or the zero-volt reference point. A bypass capacitor can be used to maintain a relatively constant dc voltage in a circuit when an ac voltage is also applied to the same point.

Procedures

1. Construct the circuit shown in Figure 44-2.

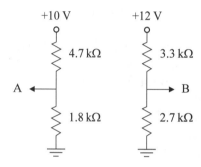

Figure 44-2

2. Measure the dc voltage at Points A and B, using the dc voltmeter.

$V_{\text{Point A}}$ = _____

$V_{\text{Point B}}$ = _____

3. Place a jumper wire between Points A and B, as shown in Figure 44-3.

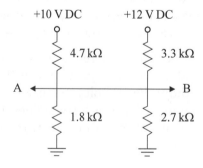

Figure 44-3

4. Measure the voltage at Point A or B with the DC voltmeter.

$V_{\text{Point A or B}}$ = _____

State your observations about the measured dc voltage in Step 2 versus the measured dc voltage in Step 4.

5. Remove the jumper wire between Points A and B and connect a 10-µF capacitor between the two points as shown in Figure 44-4.

Discussion   The 10-µF capacitor is an electrolytic capacitor; make sure that polarity is observed. Use the values measured in Step 2 to make sure that the capacitor is correctly inserted.

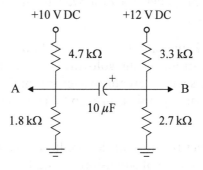

Figure 44-4

6. Measure the voltages at Points A and B with the dc voltmeter.

$V_{\text{Point A}} =$ _____

$V_{\text{Point B}} =$ _____

Using the DMM, measure the dc voltage across the capacitor.

$V_C =$ _____

State your observations about the voltages at Points A and B and the capacitor voltage, as compared to other measurements taken in Steps 2 and 4.

7. Connect the function generator and the second 10-μF capacitor as shown in Figure 44-5.

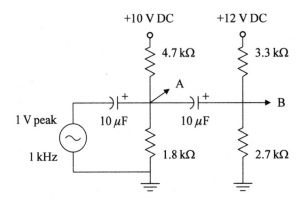

Figure 44-5

8. With the oscilloscope, measure the voltage at Point A. Make sure the AC/GND/DC switch of the oscilloscope is on **DC**. The volts/division can be set on 1 volt/division and the entire waveform should be seen. Use Channel 1.

9. Using linear graph paper draw the waveform showing the voltage amplitudes and the reference voltage.

10. Using Channel 2, measure the voltage at Point B. Make sure the AC/GND/DC switch is in the **DC** position. Set the volts/division control on a setting that allows the entire waveform to be seen. Draw this waveform in time relationship to the waveform at Point A on the same graph as in Step 9. The dual function of the oscilloscope can be used.

11. Using the subtract function of the oscilloscope, measure the voltage between Points A and B. Make sure the volts/division setting for both channels is the same. State your observations about the voltage between Points A and B.

12. Construct the circuit shown in Figure 44-6.

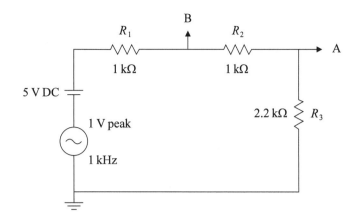

Figure 44-6

13. Measure the dc voltage across each resistor using the DMM.

$V_{R_1} =$ _____

$V_{R_2} =$ _____

$V_{R_3} =$ _____

14. Using the oscilloscope, measure the peak ac voltage at Points A and B.

$V_{\text{Point A}} =$ _____ pk

$V_{\text{Point B}} =$ _____ pk

15. Using Figure 44-7, label the voltage values, peak amplitudes, and the reference voltage that were measured across R_3.

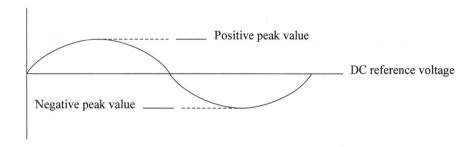

Figure 44-7

16. Insert a 10-µF capacitor across R_3 as shown in Figure 44-8.

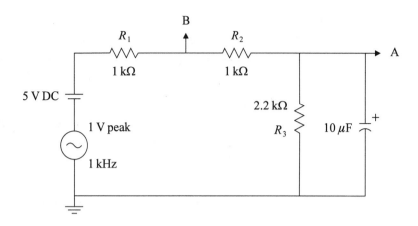

Figure 44-8

17. Compare the dc voltages across each resistor in Figure 44-8 to the dc voltages in Figure 44-6 and state your observations.

18. Measure the ac voltages at Points A and B in Figure 44-8 and compare these values to the ac values measured in Figure 44-6. State your observations.

19. Using the oscilloscope, measure the peak ac voltage that is across the dc supply and state your observations.

20. Using the DMM, measure the value of dc voltage across the ac generator and state your observations.

Observations

Using the measured values, the graphs, and your observations, answer the following questions about coupling capacitors using Figures 44-2, 44-3, 44-4, and 44-5.

1. Using Step 6 as a reference, were the dc voltages at Points A and B changed when the capacitor was inserted into the circuit?

2. Using Step 6 as a reference, determine the difference in dc voltage between the two points. Is this the dc voltage across the capacitor?

3. Were the dc voltages measured in Step 6 the same dc voltage values indicated on the waveforms as dc reference voltages?

4. What was the ac voltage value across the capacitor in Step 11?

5. Using the observation from Step 11, can there be any ac voltage across the capacitor? (*Hint: X_C*)

6. Refer to Figure 44-5. If the capacitor between Points A and B were made smaller, maybe a 0.001-μF, would there be any ac voltage across the capacitor? (If in doubt, connect a 0.001-μF and measure the ac voltage between Points A and B.)

7. Is the value of the capacitor versus the frequency of operation important when the capacitor is used as a coupling capacitor?

8. In which Step would the same dc measurements be made if the coupling capacitor were shorted?

9. Refer to Figure 44-5. If the coupling capacitor is open between Points A and B, how much ac voltage will be measured at Point A?

At Point B?

10. Refer to Figure 44-5. How much peak-to-peak voltage is indicated by the graphs at Point A?

11. Refer to Figure 44-5. How much peak-to-peak voltage is indicated by the graphs at Point B?

12. Refer to Figure 44-5. Did the coupling capacitors drop any ac voltage?

Any dc voltage?

Using Figures 44-6 and 44-8 and your observations, answer the following questions about a bypass capacitor.

13. What happened to the total dc resistance when the capacitor was inserted across R_3?

14. What happened to the total ac impedance when the capacitor was inserted across R_3?

What is the approximate ac impedance?

15. What is the approximate ac voltage across R_3 in Figure 44-6?

    In Figure 44-8?

16. Did the ac voltage across R_1 change from Figure 44-6 to Figure 44-8?

17. What caused the increase in ac voltage across R_1?

18. If a smaller capacitor, maybe a 0.001-μF, replaced the 10-μF, would the ac voltage across R_3 increase or decrease?

    Explain your answer.

19. What would happen to the dc and ac voltage across R_3 if the bypass capacitor were to open?

20. What would happen to the dc and ac voltage across R_3 if the bypass capacitor were to short?

Capacitors: Level VI

Name _____ Class _____ Date _____

Objectives   Upon completion of this experiment, you should be able to:

- Observe the effects frequency has on a complex AC RC circuit.

- Draw a functional graph of frequency versus the phase angle in various parts of a complex AC RC circuit.

- Determine the frequency at the point when the applied voltage is in-phase with the voltage across part of a complex AC RC circuit.

Text
Reference   Terrell, *Fundamentals of Electronics: DC/AC Circuits*
       Chapter 15, Sections 15-3.3 and 15-3.4

Materials
Required   Function generator (sine wave)
       Dual-trace oscilloscope
       0.0022 µF (2)
       15-kΩ resistors (2)
       Linear graph paper
       Various test leads

Introduction

Refer to Figure 45-1 for the following discussion.

The circuit shown in Figure 45-1 is a series-parallel AC RC circuit. In this circuit, the capacitor values are the same and the resistor values are the same. The series part of the circuit will cause the phase angle between the applied voltage and the total circuit current to be a negative value (fourth quadrant). The parallel part of the circuit will cause the phase angle between the applied voltage and the total circuit current to be a positive value. The size of the angle, i.e., whichever angle is greater, will determine the phase angle difference between the applied voltage and the voltage across the parallel portion of the circuit.

At some frequency, where the resistor value and the capacitive reactance value are equal, the voltage across the parallel portion of the circuit will be in-phase with the applied voltage. In this experiment, this frequency will be determined by observing the drawn graph.

Procedures

1. Construct the circuit shown in Figure 45-1.

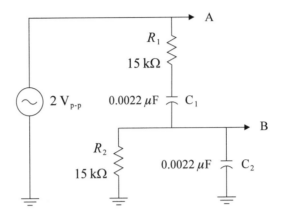

Figure 45-1

2. Lay out a sheet of linear graph paper with the X-axis as frequency, starting at 1 kHz and progressing at 1 kHz intervals to 10 kHz, and with the Y-axis as degrees, starting at −90°, (lagging behind the applied voltage) to +90° (leading the applied voltage).

Discussion   If the short side of the graph paper is placed at the bottom (frequency) and the degrees are along the long side, 18 divisions can be used to indicate 10° per division. Place the −90° at the bottom, +90° at the top of the graph, and zero degrees in the center of the Y-axis. If all of the lab teams and/or partners have the same graph, it will be easier to complete the last part of the experiment.

---

3. Connect Channel 2 of the oscilloscope to Point A and Channel 1 to Point B. Use Channel 2 as the reference voltage and place the waveform in the **standard** position.

4. Starting at 1 kHz, measure the phase angle between the applied voltage (Point A) and the voltage at Point B. Record the phase angle by placing a dot at the appropriate spot on the graph.

   Increase the frequency, at 1 kHz intervals, until the frequency is equal to 10 kHz. Determine and record each phase angle.

5. Calculate the X_C values for the frequencies in Table 45-1.

FREQUENCY	REACTANCE VALUE (X_C)
1 kHz	
3 kHz	
5 kHz	
7 kHz	
10 kHz	

Table 45-1

6. Using Figure 45-1 (the phase angle graph) and Table 45-1, determine the frequency where X_C and R are equal.

7. State your observations about the phase angle versus frequency above and below the frequency where X_C and R are equal. Be sure to include lead and lag angles with reference to the applied voltage.

8. Draw the individual phaser/vector diagrams for the series portion of the circuit and the parallel portion of the circuit at the frequency where X_C equals R.

9. Determine the percentage of the voltage at Point B, in reference to the applied voltage, at the frequency where X_C is equal to R by measurement.

$V_A = 2$ v p-p

$V_{\text{Point B}} =$ _____

_____ % of applied voltage

Observations

1. Using the observations and other data collected, compare your results with other lab teams and highlight differences between the data, stating reasons **the group** believes caused the differences. Then state ways or means that would ensure repeatable results for any lab team collecting information about the circuit in Figure 45-1 (i.e., use close tolerance components).

Capacitors: Level VII

Name_____ Class_____ Date _____

Objectives   Upon completion of this experiment, you should be able to:

• Observe the phase angle of complex RC circuits and its effect on the voltage amplitude when compared to the applied voltage.

• Observe the effect that varying the frequency and resistance has on the voltage amplitude and the phase angle.

Text   Terrell, *Fundamentals of Electronics: DC/AC Circuits*
Reference   Chapters 14 and 15

Materials   Function generator (sine wave)
Required   Dual-trace oscilloscope
3.3-kΩ resistors (2)
470-Ω resistor
5-kΩ variable resistor
0.0022-μF capacitors (2)
Various test leads

Introduction

Not all circuits have just one component that will affect the phase angle between the applied voltage and the output voltage, nor is the phase angle between the applied voltage and total circuit current the only phase angle that is of concern.

In this experiment the phase angle between the capacitor voltage and the applied voltage will be observed. There will be two RC circuits, creating a phase angle larger than 90°.

Procedures

1. Construct the circuit shown in Figure 46-1.

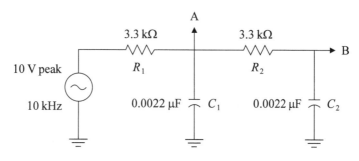

Figure 46-1

2. Connect Channel 2 of the oscilloscope across the applied voltage and Channel 1 to Point A. Determine the phase angle between the applied voltage and the voltage across the capacitor (C_1).

_____ °

Indicate the peak voltage across the capacitor (C_1).

V_{C_1} = _____ v pk

3. Connect Channel 1 at Point B. Determine the phase angle between the applied voltage and the voltage across the capacitor (C_2).

_____ °

Indicate the peak voltage across the capacitor (C_2).

V_{C_2} = _____ v pk

State why the phase angle determined in Step 3 occurred.

Discussion   The phase angle between the applied voltage and the voltage across C_1 cannot be greater than 90°. If the voltage across C_1 is the applied voltage for R_2 and C_2, then the voltage across C_2 can be −90° out-of-phase with the voltage across C_1. Therefore, if the applied voltage is compared to the voltage across C_2, we could see a −180° phase shift. By varying the frequency, we can vary the phase shift between the applied voltage and the voltage across C_2.

---

4. Remove R_1 and replace it with a 470-Ω resistor **and** a 5-kΩ variable resistor connected as a rheostat.

5. Connect Channel 2 of the oscilloscope across the applied voltage and connect Channel 1 to Point B. Slowly vary the rheostat from one limit to the other limit, monitoring the phase angle and the voltage across C_2.

State your observations; include what happens to the phase angle and V_{C_1} as the rheostat is made larger or smaller in value.

6. Remove the 470-Ω resistor and the rheostat and reinsert the 3.3-kΩ resistor.

   Slowly vary the frequency down to 1 kHz, monitoring the phase angle and the voltage across C_2.

   State your observations.

7. Slowly vary the frequency up to 100 kHz, monitoring the phase angle and the voltage across C_2.

   State your observations.

Observations

Answer the following questions based on your observations and Figure 45-1.

1. Can the applied voltage be phase shifted for a phase angle of greater than 90°?

2. What happens to the voltage across C_2 as the rheostat is made larger in value?

   Smaller in value?

3. Can the rheostat be used to control the output phase angle if it replaces R_2?

4. If the phase angle (between the applied voltage and Point B voltage) needs to be a larger value, the frequency should be adjusted to a _____ value.

5. What happened to the voltage amplitude at Point B as the frequency was increased?

As the frequency was decreased?

6. At what phase angle does the maximum output voltage occur? (*Circle the correct answer.*)

   Maximum phase angle   or   Minimum phase angle

7. Is this at a relatively low frequency or a relatively high frequency?

8. Explain your answer by showing the relationship between the reactance value and the resistance value at different frequencies.

Non-Sinusoidal Waveforms

Name_____ Class_____ Date _____

Objectives   Upon completion of this experiment, you should be able to:

- Observe the following non-sinusoidal waveforms: square wave, triangular wave, rectangular wave, and sawtooth wave.

- Measure the frequency and voltage amplitudes of the above listed waveforms.

Text   Terrell, *Fundamentals of Electronics: DC/AC Circuits*
Reference   Chapter 11, Section 11-1

Materials   Function generator (square wave and triangle wave)
Required   Percent Duty Cycle control and TTL output (optional)
Dual-trace oscilloscope

Introduction

A sine wave is a unique waveform, in that it is the only waveform that is made up of one frequency. All other waveforms are made up of the fundamental frequency (lowest frequency) and different combinations of harmonic frequencies. A harmonic frequency is a multiple of the fundamental frequency. If the fundamental frequency is 1 kHz, 2 kHz is the second harmonic, 3 kHz is the third harmonic, 4 kHz is the fourth harmonic, and so forth.

The fundamental and the harmonics are added together, at instances in time, to form different waveforms. The square wave, for example, is made up of the fundamental frequency and all the odd harmonics; 3rd, 5th, 7th, 9th, and so on. Observe Figure 47-1.

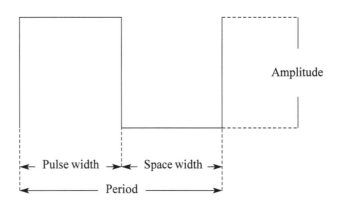

Square wave

Figure 47-1

Although the same rules apply when measuring frequency or amplitude, differences do exist in accepted standards of measurement.

This experiment will explore these differences and establish procedures for measuring any periodic non-sinusoidal waveform.

Procedures

1. Set the function generator controls to output a 1 kHz square wave.

2. Connect Channel 1 of the oscilloscope to measure the output of the function generator.

3. Adjust the amplitude control of the function generator to mid-range.

   Make sure the percent (%) duty cycle control is in the **cal** position.

4. Adjust the time/division control of the oscilloscope to 0.1 msec/division.

   Adjust the triggering level control until a stable display occurs.

Discussion   Notice that the waveform is at a positive voltage level for 5 divisions. This **time** is referred to as the pulse width. The time for the pulse width is 0.5 msec for this waveform.

$$5 \text{ divisions} \times 0.1 \text{ msec/div.} = 0.5 \text{ msec}$$

Notice that the time the waveform is at a negative voltage is also 5 divisions. This time is referred to as the space width and is also 0.5 msec.

Because the space width time is equal to the pulse width time, this waveform is referred to as a square wave. If the time/division control is adjusted one position CW, it can be observed that the waveform continually repeats the cycle. Therefore, the wave is periodic. Because the wave is periodic, the frequency of the wave can be determined.

If we add the pulse width (PW) time and the space width (SW) time together, the period (or time) for one cycle results. Taking the reciprocal of the period results in the frequency in Hertz. Other names used are pulses per second (PPS) or pulse repetition rate (PRR) or pulse recurrence frequency (PRF).

The transition from the negative voltage to the positive voltage is known as the positive transition or positive step transition. The transition from the positive voltage to the negative voltage is known as the negative transition or negative step transition.

The bottom of the waveform is referred to as the base line. All voltage amplitudes are measured from this base line.

---

5. Set the volts/division control of the oscilloscope to 2 volts/division.

   Adjust the amplitude control of the function generator until the peak level is 6 volts.

Discussion   The waveform is now three vertical divisions. Therefore, the waveform has a 6-volt peak value. Pulse waveforms are generally all positive or all negative values. Therefore, the waveform is generally measured from the base line to the most positive peak or from the zero-volt reference line to the most negative peak.

---

6. If the function generator has a percent duty cycle control, slowly adjust it to about mid-range.

Discussion   The time/division control of the oscilloscope may need to be adjusted so you can observe one or two cycles of the waveform. Notice that this waveform has a pulse width and space width that are not equal. This is a rectangular waveform shown in Figure 47-2. The waveform parameters are measured the same as for a square wave. From the point where the measurement begins to the point the cycle starts to repeat is one period; the amplitude is still measured from the baseline.

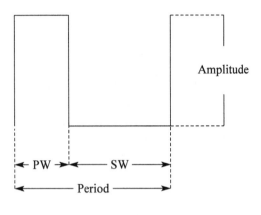

Rectangular wave

Figure 47-2

7. Adjust the percent duty cycle control to the **cal** position.

8. Select the triangle wave on the function generator. Set the output frequency for 1 kHz and the time/division of the oscilloscope to 0.1 msec/division. Adjust the triggering level until the waveform just barely starts to go positive, but still at the negtive peak, as shown in the triangle wave, Figure 47-3. It may be necessary to use the negative slope triggering.

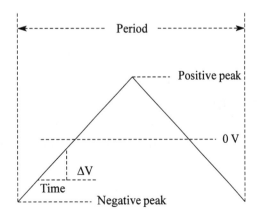

Triangle wave

Figure 47-3

Discussion   This waveform is made up of two linear ramps; a positive going ramp and a negative going ramp. Both ramps are linear because if the change in voltage versus time ratio is determined at any point on either ramp it will equal the same ratio. This linearity for both ramps defines a triangular wave.

The period for one cycle can be determined at the negative peaks as shown in Figure 47-3. The voltage amplitude is usually given by a ratio of voltage change to time, i.e., 3 volts per microsecond, or could be given as a maximum peak amplitude.

When a ratio is given as 3 volts per microsecond, it means that the voltage increases or decreases 3 volts for every microsecond. This ratio could also be stated as: 6 V/2 μsec or 1.5 V/0.5 μsec because the ratio of the change in voltage versus time is constant. Therefore, it is a linear function.

The triangular wave is sometimes used for timing controls; therefore, the major concern is the linearity of the waveform.

9. Adjust the percent duty cycle control of the function generator.

Discussion   Notice that the negative ramp of the waveform differs from the positive ramp; voltage change to time ratio. This waveform is referred to as a sawtooth waveform and is shown in Figure 47-4. The parameter measurements are made the same way as for the triangular wave.

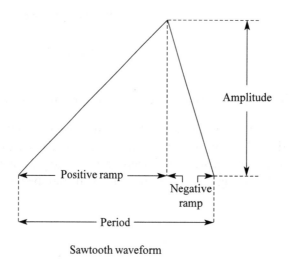

Sawtooth waveform

Figure 47-4

10. Set the function generator to output a square wave and adjust the generator for 100 kHz at 5 volts peak (from the base line).

Adjust the time/division control of the oscilloscope to display one or two cycles of the generator output.

If the oscilloscope has a Mag times 5 or 10 horizontal magnification, use it for the following observations.

Adjust the time/division and horizontal position control until the positive transition and/or the negative transition of the waveform can be displayed.

11. Observe Figure 47-5, and measure the rise and fall time values and the pulse amplitude at the points indicated by the figure.

Rise time   The time it takes for the wave to go from 10% **TO** 90% of the peak amplitude.

Fall time   The time it takes for the waveform to go from 90% **TO** 10% of the amplitude.

Pulse width   Generally measured at the 50% amplitude point.

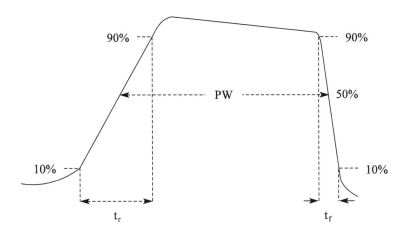

Figure 47-5

Pulse width (PW)   = _____

Rise time (t_r)   = _____

Fall time (t_f)   = _____

Integrator and Differentiator

Name_____ Class_____ Date _____

Objectives Upon completion of this experiment, you should be able to:

- Use non-sinusoidal waveforms and observe the changes that occur in the shape of the wave when applied to RC circuits.

- Determine the difference between the shape of the wave when an integrator is used as opposed to a differentiator circuit.

- Write brief theory of operations for an integrator and differentiator circuits.

Text Reference Terrell, *Fundamentals of Electronics: DC/AC Circuits*
    Chapter 15, Section 15-4

Materials Required Function generator (square wave)
Dual-trace oscilloscope
0.22-µF capacitor
0.022-µF capacitor
0.0022-µF capacitor
4.7-kΩ resistor
47-kΩ resistor
Linear graph paper (6)
Various test leads

Introduction

At times it is important to pass information on to others who may not have had an opportunity to make the observations needed to determine how a circuit works. One method to communicate this information is by using graphs accompanied by an explanation of how the results were obtained.

In this experiment passive circuits will be used to shape non-sinusoidal waveforms into other waveshapes. Graphs will be drawn to show relationships between the waveshape input into the circuit and the output waveshape. Timing relationships are just as important as the shape and amplitude of the output waveform.

Using the graphs and the circuit schematic, brief descriptions of what occurred to cause the output waveshape can be written to explain how the waveshape was created. In this experiment each half cycle will cause **events** to occur in the circuit. Writing about these events will be a major objective. In order to determine the events that occur, close observations are needed.

The close observations—collecting information, forming theories, and writing down how things occurred—are the reasons experiments are conducted.

Procedures

1. Construct the circuit shown in Figure 48-1.

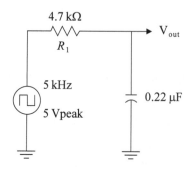

4.7 kΩ

R_1

V_{out}

5 kHz

5 Vpeak

0.22 μF

Figure 48-1

2. Determine the RC time constant.

_____ RC time constant

Determine the time the capacitor is allowed to charge and discharge (time for one-half cycle of the input).

Charge/discharge time _____ sec.

3. Using linear graph paper, draw a graph of the voltages across the capacitor and resistor showing the time relationship between these voltages and the applied voltage.

Is the time constant considered to be a long time constant or short time constant when compared to the time allowed to charge and discharge?

Discussion   The time constant is long and the output voltage is taken across the capacitor. Therefore, the circuit is an integrator.

---

4. On a separate sheet of paper describe the events that take place on each half cycle capacitor charge and discharge.

5. Replace the 0.22-μF capacitor with a 0.022-μF capacitor.

6. Using linear graph paper, draw the voltage waveshapes across the resistor and capacitor in time relationship to the input voltage.

   State why differences occurred between the waveshapes in Step 3 and Step 6. (Include time constant differences in relationship to the time to charge and discharge.)

7. Replace the 0.022-μF capacitor with a 0.22-μF capacitor.

8. Replace the 4.7-kΩ resistor with a 47-kΩ resistor.

9. Using linear graph paper draw the voltage waveshapes across the resistor and capacitor in time relationship to the input voltage.

   State why differences occurred between the waveshapes in Step 3 and Step 9. (Include time constant differences in relationship to the time to charge and discharge.)

10. Replace the 47-kΩ resistor with the 4.7-kΩ resistor.

11. Change the input frequency to 500 Hz.

Changing the input frequency has the same effect as changing the capacitor value to a _____ μF.

This is true because the relationship of the RC time constant to the time the capacitor has to charge and discharge is _____. (short/long)

12. Change the frequency to 50 kHz.

Changing the input frequency has the same effect as changing the capacitor value to a _____ μF.

This is true because the relationship of the RC time constant to the time the capacitor has to charge and discharge is _____. (short/long)

13. Construct the circuit shown in Figure 48-2.

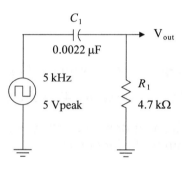

C_1

0.0022 μF

V_{out}

5 kHz

5 Vpeak

R_1

4.7 kΩ

Figure 48-2

14. Determine the RC time constant.

_____ RC time constant

Determine the time the capacitor is allowed to charge and discharge (time for one-half cycle of the input).

Charge/discharge time _____ sec.

15. Using linear graph paper, draw a graph of the voltages across the capacitor and resistor showing the time relationship between these voltages and the applied voltage.

Is the time constant considered to be a long time constant or short time constant when compared to the time allowed to charge and discharge?

Discussion   The time constant is short and the output voltage is taken across the resistor. Therefore, the circuit is a differentiator circuit.

16. On a separate sheet of paper, describe the events that take place on each half cycle of capacitor charge and discharge. Include the resistor voltage value, (2 times volts peak?).

17. Replace the 0.0022-μF capacitor with a 0.022-μF capacitor.

18. Using linear graph paper, draw the voltage waveshapes across the resistor and capacitor in time relationship to the input voltage.

    State why differences occurred between the waveshapes in Step 15 and Step 19. (Include time constant differences in relationship to the time to charge and discharge.)

19. Replace the 0.022-μF capacitor with a 0.0022-μF capacitor.

20. Replace the 4.7-kΩ resistor with a 47-kΩ resistor.

21. Using linear graph paper, draw the voltage waveshapes across the resistor and capacitor in time relationship to the input voltage.

    State why differences occurred between the waveshapes in Step 15 and Step 21. (Include time constant differences in relationship to the time to charge and discharge.)

22. Replace the 47-kΩ resistor with the 4.7-kΩ resistor.

23. Change the input frequency to 500 Hz.

    Changing the input frequency has the same effect as changing the capacitor value to a
    _____ μF.

    This is true because the relationship of the RC time constant to the time the capacitor
    has to charge and discharge is _____. (short/long)

Series AC RCL Circuits: Level I

Name_____ Class_____ Date _____

Objectives	Upon completion of this experiment, you should be able to:

- Observe the characteristics of a series AC RCL circuit operating at frequencies that will cause the circuit to act capacitively, or will cause the circuit to act inductively.

- Determine by experimentation, the phase angle between the circuit current and applied voltage, the individual voltage drops, and the value of circuit current.

- Observe changes in the characteristics as variations are made in circuit components or frequency.

Text Reference	Terrell, *Fundamentals of Electronics: DC/AC Circuits* Chapter 16, Sections 16-1 and 16-2
Materials Required	Function generator (sine wave) Dual-trace oscilloscope 100-mH inductor 33-mH inductor 0.022-µF capacitor 1.8-kΩ resistor 390-Ω resistor Linear graph paper Various test leads

Introduction

Important points to remember:

- The current through a resistor and the voltage across a resistor are always in-phase.

- In a inductive circuit the applied voltage leads the resistor voltage.

- In a capacitive circuit the applied voltage lags the resistor voltage.

When an inductor and a capacitor are in series with a resistor, the larger reactive component will control the phase angle between the applied voltage and the circuit current. The larger reactive component will also have the larger reactive voltage. The capacitive reactive voltage will be −90° out-of-phase with the voltage across the resistor, whereas the inductive reactive voltage will be +90° out-of-phase with the voltage across the resistor. The net reactive voltage will be used to determine the phase angle between the applied voltage and the circuit current. This indicates that the larger reactive component will determine whether the applied voltage leads or lags the total circuit current.

The larger reactive component will be determined by the size of the components and the frequency of the applied voltage. As has been observed in previous experiments, as frequency increases the reactance of the capacitor decreases and the reactance of the inductor increases. This indicates that the circuit can act capacitively or inductively, depending on the frequency.

Procedures

1. Measure the actual values of the resistors with the ohmmeter.

   $R_{390\ \Omega}$ = _____

   $R_{1.8\ k\Omega}$ = _____

2. Construct the circuit shown in Figure 49-1.

3. Connect the external trigger input of the oscilloscope to Point A of the circuit. Place the triggering source switch to the EXT. position.

Discussion   The external trigger of the oscilloscope will maintain a constant time reference. This will allow all the measured voltages to have the same time reference. Therefore, a phase angle comparison can be made to the applied voltage, even if the subtract function of the oscilloscope is being used. Remember, if the subtract function is being used, the channel that is being used to trigger the oscilloscope is being moved. Every time the probe is moved the time reference changes. Therefore, a constant time reference is needed.

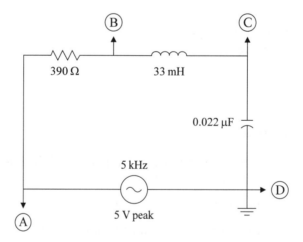

Figure 49-1

4. Connect Channel 2 to Point A and adjust the triggering level control, vertical position control, horizontal position control, and time base selector until the waveform at Point A is in the standard position.

After the waveform is in the standard position, **do not** adjust the triggering level control. If the control is inadvertently adjusted, repeat the above stated step to make sure that the waveform at Point A is in the standard position.

Note   Take note of where the input waveform crosses the X-axis or when it is at 180°. This will be the point used to determine the phase angle.

5. Set up the oscilloscope for the subtract function, remembering that the channel that can be inverted will be referred to as Channel 1 and the non-inverted channel will be referred to as Channel 2. Use Channel 1 as the ground lead of the voltmeter and Channel 2 as the probe or red lead.

Discussion   The reference voltage is the applied voltage. Any voltage measured will be time referenced to this voltage. If the number of degrees per division and the number of divisions difference between when one waveform is at 180° and another waveform is at 180° are known, the phase angle between the two waveforms can be determined. The point on the X-axis where the reference waveform is at 180° is already known.

6. Measure the voltage across the capacitor, placing Channel 2 at Point C and Channel 1 at Point D. Determine the phase shift angle and the peak voltage and record both in Table 49-1.

Discussion   For clarity, if the voltage is lagging the applied voltage, indicate this by placing a minus sign in front of the angle. This will be a quick indicator for the purposes of this experiment.

7. Measure the voltage across the inductor, placing Channel 2 at Point B and Channel 1 at Point C. Determine the phase shift angle and the peak voltage and record both in Table 49-1.

8. Measure the voltage across the resistor, placing Channel 2 at Point A and Channel 1 at Point B. Determine the phase shift angle and the peak voltage and record both in Table 49-1.

COMPONENT	VOLTS PEAK	PHASE SHIFT
Capacitor		
Inductor		
Resistor		

Table 49-1

9. Using the applied voltage as a time reference and linear graph paper, draw the voltage waveform across each component and indicate the phase shift between each component voltage. Use the applied voltage as the reference waveform.

10. If the frequency of the applied voltage is increased, but not above 6 kHz, what will happen to the following: (increase ↑, decrease ↓, or remains the same ↔).

    Net reactance _____

    Phase shift between current and applied voltage _____

    Circuit current _____

    Resistor voltage _____

11. Increase the frequency to confirm the answers, remembering not to go above 6 kHz.

12. If the frequency of the applied voltage is decreased, what will happen to the following: (increase ↑, decrease ↓, or remains the same ↔).

    Net reactance _____

    Phase shift between current and applied voltage _____

    Circuit current _____

    Resistor voltage _____

13. Decrease the frequency to confirm the answers.

14. Construct the circuit shown in Figure 49-2.

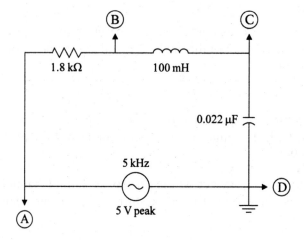

Figure 49-2

15. Measure the voltage across the capacitor, placing Channel 2 at Point C and Channel 1 at Point D. Determine the phase shift angle and the peak voltage and record both in Table 49-2.

16. Measure the voltage across the inductor, placing Channel 2 at Point B and Channel 1 at Point C. Determine the phase angle and the peak voltage and record both in Table 49-2.

17. Measure the voltage across the resistor, placing Channel 2 at Point A and Channel 1 at Point B. Determine the phase shift angle and the peak voltage and record both in Table 49-2.

COMPONENT	VOLTS PEAK	PHASE SHIFT
Capacitor		
Inductor		
Resistor		

Table 49-2

18. Using the applied voltage as a time reference and linear graph paper, draw the voltage waveform across each component and indicate the phase shift between each component voltage.

Observations

Answer the following questions, using the information in Table 49-1 and the graphs.

1. Is the circuit acting capacitively or inductively?

2. In a series circuit, which reactive component will determine the phase angle between the current and applied voltage? (The component with the smallest or largest reactance?)

3. Determine the circuit current value. (Ignore the r_s value of the inductor and use the actual measured value of the resistor.)

4. Using the current determined in Question 3, determine the value of X_C and X_L.

5. Using the values determined in Question 4, determine the net reactance.

6. Using the net reactance, determine the voltage that should be measured across the inductor and capacitor.

Answer the following questions, using the information in Table 49-2 and the graphs.

7. Is the circuit acting capacitively or inductively?

8. Explain the answer indicated in Question 7.

9. Determine the circuit current value. (Ignore the r_s value of the inductor and use the actual measured value of the resistor.)

10. Using the current determined in Question 9, determine the value of X_C and X_L.

11. Using the values determined in Question 10, determine the net reactance.

12. Using the net reactance determined in Question 11, determine the voltage that should be measured across the inductor and capacitor.

13. If the frequency of the applied voltage is decreased, but not below 3 kHz, what will happen to the following: (increase ↑, decrease ↓, or remains the same ↔).

    Net reactance _____

    Phase shift between current and applied voltage _____

    Circuit current _____

    Resistor voltage _____

14. Decrease the frequency to confirm the answers, remembering not to go below 3 kHz.

15. If the frequency of the applied voltage is increased, what will happen to the following: (increase ↑, decrease ↓, or remains the same ↔).

    Net reactance _____

    Phase shift between current and applied voltage _____

    Circuit current _____

    Resistor voltage _____

16. Increase the frequency to confirm the answers.

Series AC RCL Circuits: Resonance; Level II

Name_____ Class_____ Date _____

Objectives   Upon completion of this experiment, you should be able to:

- Determine, experimentally, the frequency of resonance in a series RCL circuit.

- Observe the resonant characteristics.

- Draw a functional graph of frequency versus voltage and determine from the graph the edge or cutoff frequencies, the bandwidth, and the Q of the circuit.

- Discover if there is a difference between the center frequency and the resonant frequency.

Text Reference   Terrell, *Fundamentals of Electronics: DC/AC Circuits*
      Chapter 16, Sections 16-2 and 16-3

Materials Required   Function generator
Dual-trace oscilloscope
330-Ω resistor
150-Ω resistor
33-mH inductor
0.0022-μF capacitor
Linear graph paper
Various test leads

Introduction

When the reactance of the capacitor and the reactance of the inductor are equal, the net reactance is zero. Therefore, the circuit acts resistively. The voltage across the series resistance is equal to the applied voltage and the current is at its maximum value. When this occurs, the circuit is at the resonant frequency. The theoretical resonant frequency can be determined by the following equation:

$$f_r = \frac{1}{2 \pi \sqrt{L\ C}}$$

This equation determines the frequency where X_C is equal to X_L. Because both reactances are 180° out-of-phase, the reactances cancel. The size of the series resistance determines the circuit current. This causes a large voltage across both the inductor and the capacitor. These voltages are also 180° out-of-phase. Because the reactances cancel each other, the circuit current and the applied voltage are in-phase.

When the operating frequency is at or near the resonant frequency, the circuit current causes the voltage across the resistor to be at a maximum value. Using this voltage, a graph can be drawn showing the band of frequencies that causes a higher voltage drop across the resistor. This voltage can be monitored with the oscilloscope and the frequency of resonance determined by experimentation.

Associated with the resonant frequency is the bandwidth. This bandwidth is determined when the values of voltage across the resistor are determined. If the maximum voltage across the resistor is known, the frequencies inside the bandwidth can be determined by multiplying the maximum voltage by 0.707. When this value of voltage is determined, you should note that it occurs at two frequencies; a lower frequency called f_1 and a higher frequency f_2. The difference between these two frequencies is the bandwidth.

Once the bandwidth is known, the Q (quality of merit) can be calculated by the following equation:

$$\frac{f_{resonance}}{Bandwidth} = Q$$

Notice that as the bandwidth increases, with a constant resonant frequency, the Q will decrease. The Q value can also be approximated by the following equation:

$$\frac{X_L}{r_s} = Q$$

where r_s is the series resistance of the inductor and any resistor that is also in series with the inductor.

Procedures

1. Measure the dc series resistance (r_s) of the inductor.

   $r_s =$ _____ Ω

2. Construct the circuit shown in Figure 50-1.

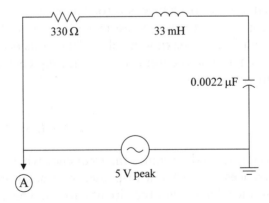

Figure 50-1

3. Connect the external trigger to Point A and set the triggering source control to EXT.

4. Set the function generator for 10 kHz at 5 v peak.

    Connect Channel 2 to Point A and put the waveform in the standard position.

5. Using the subtract function of the oscilloscope, measure the peak voltage across the resistor and determine the phase shift between the circuit current and applied voltage.

    Record these values in the spaces provided in Table 50-1.

FREQUENCY	VOLTS PEAK	PHASE ANGLE
10 kHz		
11 kHz		
12 kHz		
13 kHz		
14 kHz		
15 kHz		
16 kHz		
17 kHz		
18 kHz		
19 kHz		
20 kHz		
21 kHz		
22 kHz		
23 kHz		
24 kHz		
25 kHz		

Table 50-1

6. Repeat Steps 4 and 5 for each frequency listed in Table 50-1.

7. Lay out the linear graph paper as follows:

    Use the long side as the frequency (label the bottom) and the short side as voltage (label the left-hand side).

    Each major division equals 1 kHz and 0.3 volts.

8. Plot the voltage at each frequency on the graph.

    Draw a smooth line connecting the plots.

9. Using the table and the graph, state your observations about the voltage across the resistor and the phase angle at the different frequencies. Include in the observations whether the circuit is acting capacitively or inductively and at what frequencies. (Use Experiment 49 as a reference if in doubt.)

   Compare the observations to other lab teams and list and discuss reasons for the results.

10. Change the resistor to a 150-Ω resistor.

    Repeat Steps 4–8, using Table 50-2.

11. Compare the results of the two graphs and state what values changed and what values did not change. Explain why values changed or did not change.

FREQUENCY	VOLTS PEAK	PHASE ANGLE
10 kHz		
11 kHz		
12 kHz		
13 kHz		
14 kHz		
15 kHz		
16 kHz		
17 kHz		
18 kHz		
19 kHz		
20 kHz		
21 kHz		
22 kHz		
23 kHz		
24 kHz		
25 kHz		

Table 50-2

Observations

1. For each **graph** calculate the following and explain or show how each value was determined.

   Resonant frequency: Graph 1

   Resonant frequency: Graph 2

Edge frequencies: Graph 1

Edge frequencies: Graph 2

Bandwidth: Graph 1

Bandwidth: Graph 2

Q of the circuit: Graph 1

Q of the circuit: Graph 2

2. Determine the algebraic center frequencies (both graphs) by:

$$\frac{f_1 + f_2}{2} = f_{center}$$

Determine the geometric center frequencies (both graphs) by:

$$\sqrt{f_1 \cdot f_2} = f_{center}$$

State which method comes closer to the actual resonant frequency determined by the graph.

Discussion   The following equations are provided for convenience:

$$f_r = \frac{0.159}{\sqrt{LC}}$$

$$BW \times Q = f_r$$

The edge frequencies occur when the graph voltage is 70% of the maximum graph voltage. The center frequency will occur when the maximum voltage occurs across the resistor.

Parallel RCL Circuits: Level I

Name_____ Class_____ Date _____

Objectives   Upon completion of this experiment, you should be able to:

- Observe the characteristics of a parallel AC RCL circuit. The following will be observed:

  - phase angle of total circuit current versus applied voltage

  - phase angle of the current through each reactive component versus the voltage across that component

  - effect changing the frequency has on the total circuit current to applied voltage phase angle

  - effect changing the components has on the total circuit current to applied voltage phase angle

- Practice using the oscilloscope's external trigger to measure phase angles.

Text   Terrell, *Fundamentals of Electronics: DC/AC Circuits*
Reference   Chapter 16, Sections 16-1.2, 16-2.2, and 16-3

Materials   Function generator (sine wave)
Required   Dual-trace oscilloscope
100-mH inductor
33-mH inductor
0.0047-µF capacitor
0.001-µF capacitor
2.7-kΩ resistor
220-Ω resistor
Various test leads

Introduction

In a parallel capacitive, inductive, and resistive circuit, the current vectors or phasors are used to determine the phase angle between the applied voltage and total circuit current. The smallest component will have control over how the circuit acts or whether the circuit current leads or lags the applied voltage. Because the components are in parallel, the voltage across each component is the same and is in-phase with the applied voltage.

In this experiment a small resistor will be placed in series with each branch to determine the phase angle between the applied voltage and each branch current. This resistor will introduce a small error into the theoretical values and the practical values.

Procedures

1. Construct the circuit shown in Figure 51-1, installing the jumper wires as shown.

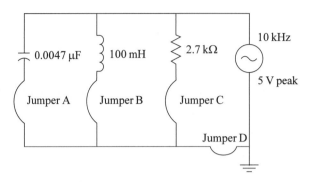

Figure 51-1

2. Connect the oscilloscope external trigger across the applied voltage and connect Channel 2 to measure the applied voltage. Adjust the controls of the oscilloscope to put the waveform in the standard position.

3. Remove Jumper A and place a 220-Ω resistor in the **gap** left by the removal of the jumper.

4. With the oscilloscope in the dual mode, connect Channel 1 between the capacitor and the 220-Ω resistor to measure this voltage.

Discussion   The resistor in series with the capacitor will effect the phase angle slightly but not enough for the observations needed. The voltage across the resistor will be small compared to the capacitor voltage, about 180 mv pk. Remember that the voltage across the 220-Ω resistor represents the phase of the current through the capacitor.

---

5. Observe Channel 1, measuring the phase angle difference as compared to the applied voltage.

   Is the current through the capacitor leading or lagging the applied voltage, by your observation?

6. Remove the 220-Ω resistor and replace Jumper A. Remove Jumper B and place the 220-Ω resistor in the gap.

7. Place Channel 1 at the inductor-resistor junction.

   Measure the phase angle difference between the current through the inductor (the voltage across the 220-Ω resistor) and the applied voltage.

   Is the current through the inductor leading or lagging the applied voltage, by your observation?

8. Remove the 220-Ω resistor and replace Jumper B.

9. Remove Jumper C and place the 220-Ω resistor in the gap.

   Place Channel 1 at the resistor-resistor junction.

   Measure the phase angle difference between the current through the resistor and the applied voltage.

   Is the current through the resistor leading, lagging, or in-phase with the applied voltage, by your observation?

10. Remove the 220-Ω resistor and replace Jumper C.

    Remove Jumper D and place the 220-Ω resistor in the gap.

11. Measure the voltage across the 220-Ω resistor.

    Is the total circuit current leading or lagging the applied voltage, by your observation?

    Is the circuit acting capacitively or inductively?

Discussion   Remember, in a parallel circuit the smallest component has more control because the current is larger through that component.

Determine the net reactive current in this circuit by drawing the current phasor diagram for the circuit.

Notice that the capacitive current is larger than the inductive current. Therefore, the total circuit current leads the applied voltage.

The calculated phase angle should be larger than the measured phase angle. In the calculations, the series dc resistance of the inductor and the 220-Ω resistor were not considered in the calculations.

The phase angle between the current through the inductor and the applied voltage should not have been 90°, as expected, due to the series resistances. The capacitor current phase angle should have been closer to 90° than the inductor current and the current through the resistor should have been in-phase with the applied voltage. The total circuit current should have been approximately 45°.

12. Connect Channel 2 to measure the applied voltage with Channel 1 measuring the voltage across the 220-Ω resistor.

Slowly vary the frequency down to about 4 kHz. State your observations about the phase angle between the applied voltage and the total circuit current. Include in the observations whether the circuit is acting capacitively or inductively as the frequency is decreased?

13. Construct the circuit shown in Figure 51-2.

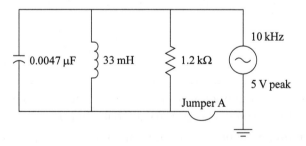

Figure 51-2

14. Draw the current phasor diagram that represents the circuit shown in Figure 51-2. Determine the total circuit current to applied voltage phase angle.

15. Remove Jumper A and place the 220-Ω resistor in the gap.

Connect Channel 2 to measure the applied voltage and Channel 1 to measure the voltage across the 220-Ω resistor.

Determine the phase angle between the total circuit current and the applied voltage.

16. Slowly vary the frequency up to about 15 kHz. State your observations about the phase angle and whether the circuit is acting capacitively or inductively as the frequency approaches 15 kHz.

Note The 220-Ω resistor should remain installed for the following steps. The oscilloscope should be measuring the applied voltage on Channel 2 and the voltage across the 220-Ω resistor on Channel 1.

17. Set the function generator frequency to 10 kHz.

Replace the 0.0047-µF capacitor with the 0.001-µF capacitor. State your observations about the phase angle and whether the inductor or capacitor has the largest current, by your observations.

18. Remove the 1.2-kΩ resistor and do not replace the resistor. State your observations about the effect the resistor has on the phase angle between the applied voltage and the total circuit current. Include in your observations the value of the total circuit current before and after the 1.2-kΩ resistor was removed from the circuit.

19. Put a 120-Ω resistor in place of the 1.2-kΩ resistor and state your observations about the phase angle and the value of the total circuit current.

Parallel RCL Circuit: Resonance; Level II

Name _____ Class _____ Date _____

Objectives	Upon completion of this experiment, you should be able to:

- Observe the characteristics of a parallel resonant circuit, including: circuit Q, bandwidth, edge frequencies, total circuit current to applied voltage phase angle, and resonant frequency and/or center frequency.

- Observe what effect the series resistor has on bandwidth and *Q*.

- Draw a functional graph of frequency versus voltage across the resistor to determine the stated characteristics.

- Determine the phase angle of a parallel RCL circuit above or below the frequency of resonance.

Text Reference	Terrell, *Fundamentals of Electronics: DC/AC Circuits* Chapter 16, Sections 16-1.2, 16-2.2, and 16-3
Materials Required	Function generator (sine wave) Dual-trace oscilloscope 33-mH inductor 10-mH inductor 0.033-µF capacitor 100-Ω resistor 1-kΩ resistor 10-kΩ resistor Linear graph paper Various test leads

Introduction

Like the series resonant circuit, the resonant frequency occurs when the capacitive reactance value is equal to the inductive reactance value. However, the voltage across the capacitive and inductive reactances are the same, they are in parallel. The currents for each reactive branch are 180° out-of-phase with each other and they cancel. The reactive component that is the smallest value will determine how the circuit acts; inductively or capacitively. At the resonant frequency there is no reactive current and the applied voltage and circuit current are in-phase. This indicates that a resonant rise in impedance occurs because the current will be at its minimum value.

To experimentally determine the value of the resonant frequency, a resistor is placed in series with the parallel reactive components. Monitoring the resistor voltage will result in minimum resistor voltage at the frequency of resonance. From a graph of the resistor voltage, the bandwidth and *Q* of the circuit can be determined using the same equations as used in Experiment 50.

Procedures

1. Construct the circuit shown in Figure 52-1.

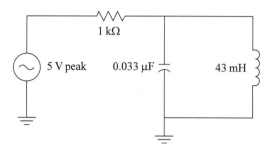

Figure 52-1

The 43-mH coil is a 33-mH coil in series with a 10-mH coil.

2. Connect the external trigger input of the oscilloscope to the applied voltage. Set the oscilloscope controls to use the subtract function and connect Channel 2 to measure the applied voltage and Channel 1 to measure the voltage across the parallel LC circuit.

3. In the subtract mode, measure the voltage amplitude across the resistor and the phase angle at each frequency listed in Table 52-1. Indicate whether the current is lagging the applied voltage by indicating a negative angle or leading the applied voltage by indicating a positive angle.

4. Using linear graph paper, plot a functional graph of frequency versus voltage. Use the long side of the paper (24 divisions) for the frequency (X-axis) and the short side as voltage (Y-axis).

5. Adjust the frequency until the voltage across the resistor is at its minimum value and the phase angle is as close to zero degrees as possible.

   Mark this frequency on the graph as the resonant frequency.

6. Decrease the frequency until the resistor voltage is at its maximum value.

   _____ v pk

   Return the generator frequency to the frequency determined in Step 5.

   Decrease the frequency of the generator until the resistor voltage is equal to 70% of the maximum resistor voltage, Step 6, and the phase angle is as close to 45° as possible.

   Mark this frequency on the graph as the lower cutoff or edge frequency.

7. Increase the frequency until the resistor voltage is at its maximum value.

   _____ v pk

   Return the generator frequency to the frequency determined in Step 5.

   Increase the frequency of the generator until the resistor voltage is equal to 70% of the maximum resistor voltage and the phase angle is as close to 45° as possible.

   Mark this frequency on the graph as the upper cutoff or edge frequency.

FREQUENCY	RESISTOR VOLTAGE	V_A TO I_T PHASE ANGLE
2 kHz		
3 kHz		
4 kHz		
5 kHz		
6 kHz		
7 kHz		
8 kHz		
9 kHz		
10 kHz		
11 kHz		
12 kHz		
13 kHz		
14 kHz		
15 kHz		
16 kHz		
17 kHz		
18 kHz		
19 kHz		
20 kHz		
21 kHz		
22 kHz		
23 kHz		
24 kHz		
25 kHz		

Table 52-1

8. Determine the bandwidth from the values in Steps 6 and 7.

$$f_2 - f_1 = BW$$

9. From the values determined in Steps 5 and 8, determine the Q of the circuit.

$$Q = \frac{f_r}{BW}$$

10. Measure the voltage across the parallel LC circuit, using Channel 1 (non-inverted). Indicating the voltage and phase angle at each frequency listed in Table 52-2.

FREQUENCY	REACTIVE VOLTAGE	V_A TO V_{LC} PHASE ANGLE
2 kHz		
3 kHz		
4 kHz		
5 kHz		
6 kHz		
7 kHz		
8 kHz		
9 kHz		
10 kHz		
11 kHz		
12 kHz		
13 kHz		
14 kHz		
15 kHz		
16 kHz		
17 kHz		
18 kHz		
19 kHz		
20 kHz		
21 kHz		
22 kHz		
23 kHz		
24 kHz		
25 kHz		

Table 52-2

11. Using the same graph as in Step 4, plot the voltage indicated at each frequency.

Compare the values determined in Steps 5 through 9 with the values determined by using the voltage across the parallel LC circuit. State your observations about the following. (Be sure to include whether the values appeared to increase, decrease, or remained the same.)

Frequency of resonance:

Edge or cutoff frequencies:

Bandwidth:

Q of the circuit:

12. Change the series resistor to a 100-Ω resistor and measure the voltage across the parallel LC circuit at different frequencies to determine if the bandwidth and the Q of the circuit have changed. Use Steps 5 through 9 as a reference to measure these values.

The Q of the circuit is now:

The bandwidth of the circuit is now:

13. Change the series resistor to a 10-kΩ resistor and measure the voltage across the parallel LC circuit at different frequencies to determine if the bandwidth and the Q of the circuit have changed. Use Steps 5 through 9 as a reference to measure these values.

    The Q of the circuit is now:

    The bandwidth of the circuit is now:

14. State the effect the series resistor has on the edge frequencies, bandwidth, and the Q of the circuit.

    Does the series resistor affect the resonant frequency? Explain your answer.

15. Replace the series 10-kΩ resistor with a 1-kΩ resistor.

    Remove the 10-mH coil used to make the 43-mH coil and place a jumper wire in the gap.

16. Determine the resonant frequency by measuring the voltage across the parallel LC circuit and state your observations.

17. Determine the bandwidth and the Q of the circuit.

    Compare the values in Steps 16 and 17 to the values in Steps 5 through 9 and state your observations. Include in your observations why the value of Q and the bandwidth changed as well as the resonant frequency.

Observations

1. Based on Table 52-1, Table 52-2, and other observations, state what happens to the phase angle between the applied voltage and total circuit current above, below, and at resonance.

2. State your observations about the impedance of a parallel LC circuit above, below, and at resonance.

3. State your observations about the voltage and current across and through the resistor and the parallel LC circuit above, below, and at resonance.

Transformers: Power; Level I

Name_____ Class_____ Date_____

Objectives   Upon completion of this experiment, you should be able to:

- Observe the basic characteristics of a power transformer.

- Determine the turns ratio, given the secondary voltage.

- Determine, experimentally, the turns ratio.

- Determine the primary and secondary currents, given the required load conditions.

- Determine the proper size fuse, after obtaining sufficient information about the secondary load conditions.

Text   Terrell, *Fundamentals of Electronics: DC/AC Circuits*
Reference   Chapter 17, Sections 17-2 and 17-3

Materials   12.6 VAC center-tapped power transformer
Required   Dual-trace oscilloscope
               AC voltmeter
               AC current meter
               470-Ω resistors (2)

Introduction

⚠ **CAUTION** **During this experiment you will be required to measure the line voltage that connects to the power transformer. Extra care is needed when measuring voltages that are lethal. Make sure that the DMM or other voltmeter is set correctly and that someone monitors your voltage measurement. Use probes that can be inserted into the outlet if your transformer is enclosed.**

For help in calculating the turns ratio, voltage primary to voltage secondary, current primary to current secondary, impedance in the secondary to impedance in the primary, and transformer efficiency, refer to the equations at the end of the experiment.

Procedures

1. Using the values in Figure 53-1, determine the turns ratio of the transformer (primary-to-secondary).

_____ : _____

  Primary   : Secondary

Figure 53-1

2. Using Figure 53-2 as a reference, measure the line voltage using the DMM, V_{AB} or the full secondary voltage, V_{AC} or the voltage from one side to the center tap, and V_{BC} or the voltage from the other side of the secondary to the center tap. Measure these values using the ac voltmeter (DMM). Record these values in the spaces provided in Figure 53-2.

Now determine the actual turns ratio of the transformer, using the measured values. Place the values in the provided spaces in Figure 53-2.

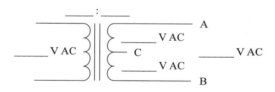

Figure 53-2

3. State your observations about the theoretical values as compared to the actual measured values. Include reasons why there are differences. (*Hint:* Compensation for the transformer losses.)

Discussion   The turns ratio for the practical value should be somewhat higher than the stated value. The reason for this is to compensate for transformer losses when the transformer is under a heavy current load. Providing a few extra turns helps compensate for any losses due to eddy currents, hystersis loses, and other factors.

Because the power in the primary is equal to the power in the secondary, when the voltage is stepped down the current has to be stepped up. The current ratio is, therefore, the reciprocal of the voltage turns ratio.

Most transformers have a rated efficiency. The efficiency is determined by dividing the secondary power by the primary power and multiplying by 100. See the equation at the end of the experiment. This indicates the transformers efficiency.

4. Construct the circuit shown in Figure 53-3.

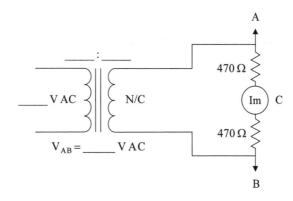

Figure 53-3

5. Record the previously measured primary voltage and measure the secondary voltages as indicated in the figure.

Record the secondary current as measured by the ac current meter I_m.

I_m indicates = _____ mA

6. Using the secondary voltage V_{AB} measured in Step 5 and the previously measured primary voltage, determine the turns ratio for the transformer. Indicate the turns ratio on the provided spaces in Figure 53-3.

Is the turns ratio different under loaded conditions (Steps 5 and 6) as compared to the unloaded conditions in Steps 1 and 2?

7. Using the turns ratio determined in Step 6 and indicated secondary current, determine the primary current.

$I_P =$ _____

If a fuse is used in the secondary, what is the minimum size required?

If a fuse is used in the primary, what is the minimum size required?

8. Determine the power in the primary and the power in the secondary, using the values determined in Steps 5 and 7 and the previously measured primary voltage.

Determine the transformer efficiency.

9. Using the oscilloscope, connect Channel 1 to measure the waveform from Point A to Point C in Figure 53-3. Either side of the secondary can be Point A.

Connect Channel 2 to measure the waveform from Point B to Point C and state your observations about the two waveforms.

Discussion   The following formulas are provided for convenience:

$$Power_{primary} = Power_{secondary}$$

$$\frac{N_p}{N_s} = \frac{V_p}{V_s} = \frac{I_s}{I_p} = \sqrt{\frac{Z_p}{Z_s}}$$

$$\frac{Power_{secondary}}{Power_{primary}} = 100 = \%\ efficiency$$

Transformers: Audio Impedance Matching; Level II

Name _____ Class _____ Date _____

Objectives   Upon completion of this experiment, you should be able to:

- Determine the turns ratio of an audio impedance matching transformer.

- Observe the impedance matching characteristics of a audio transformer.

- Match the impedance of the function generator by using the audio transformer.

Text
Reference   Terrell, *Fundamentals of Electronics: DC/AC Circuits*
          Chapter 17, Section 17-4

Materials
Required   Audio transformer (impedance matching)
          Function generator (sine wave)
          AC voltmeter
          AC current meter
          Dual-trace oscilloscope
          Various test leads
          8-Ω speaker

Introduction

Transformers are usually used to increase or decrease the voltage supplied to circuits. Another application of the transformer is to make the impedance of a load look larger than its actual value—impedance matching. Impedance matching causes maximum transfer of power from one point in the circuit to another point in the circuit.

In some cases dc isolation is required where an audio signal is being passed from one point in the circuit to another point in the circuit. Consider the application of a speaker. An increase in current can be gained by using the isolation transformer.

A common speaker has an impedance of 8 ohms at 1 kHz. Most amplifiers cannot supply enough current at this impedance to allow the speaker to be heard; therefore, if the impedance is increased, the current can be smaller and still deliver the maximum power to the speaker.

Procedures

1. Construct the circuit shown in Figure 54-1.

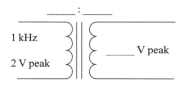

Figure 54-1

2. Apply a signal to the primary from the function generator. Using the oscilloscope to measure the primary and secondary voltages, determine the turns ratio of the transformer. Record the value in the provided places in Figure 54-1.

3. Construct the circuit shown in Figure 54-2.

Determine the current in the secondary by dividing the voltage across the 470-Ω resistor by the resistor value.

$I_{sec.}$ _____

The ac current meter should indicate the current through the primary.

$I_{pri.}$ = _____

Using the primary voltage and the primary current value, determine the primary impedance.

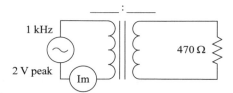

Figure 54-2

Z_p = _____

Using the following equation and the determined turns ratio (Step 2), calculate the theoretical primary impedance.

$$\frac{(470 \ \Omega)(N_p{}^2)}{N_s{}^2} = Z_p$$

State your observations about the impedance values.

4. Construct the circuit shown in Figure 54-3. The amplitude of the function generator may need to be increased to hear the 1-kHz tone.

Figure 54-3

Vary the amplitude of the function generator and note the loudness of the tone.

5. Construct the circuit shown in Figure 54-4 and state the differences noted in amplitude versus the loudness of the tone.

Figure 54-4

EQUIPMENT LIST

Digital Multimeter @ 10 MΩ input impedance

Volt-Ohm-Meter @ 20 kΩ/volt

Dual DC Power Supply @ 0 to 20 volts DC

Function Generator @ 50 Ω output impedance
        DC offset on/off
        Sine Wave . . Triangle Wave . . Square Wave
        Percent Duty Cycle Adjustment
        TTL Output

Dual-Trace Oscilloscope @ 20 MHz

OPTIONAL

1-10-100 mA Current Meter

Capacitance Meter

COMPONENTS

$\frac{1}{4}$ W Resistor Kit

or

2 MΩ
100 kΩ
47 kΩ
10 kΩ
8.2 kΩ
6.8 kΩ
5.6 kΩ
4.7 kΩ
3.3 kΩ
2.7 kΩ (2)
2.2 kΩ
1.5 kΩ
1 kΩ (3)
820 Ω
680 Ω
560 Ω
470 Ω
330 Ω
220 Ω
180 Ω (2)
150 Ω
100 Ω
56 Ω (2)

Capacitors

1000 µF 50 V
100 µF 50 V
10 µF 35 V (2)
2.2 µF 35 V
0.22 µF 35 V
0.1 µF 35 V
0.033 µF 35 V
0.022 µF 35 V
0.01 µF 35 V
0.0047 µF 35 V
0.0033 µF 35 V
0.0022 µF 35 V (2)
0.001 µF 35 V

Inductors

4 to 7H
100 mH
33 mH
10 mH
1 mH

Variable Resistors

100 kΩ
20 kΩ
10 kΩ (2)
5 kΩ
1 kΩ

Switches/Misc.

SPST switch
SPDT switch
Neon Tube NE2
Red LED
Green LED

12 volt DPDT relay
3 volt DPDT relay
   1N914 or 1N4148 (small
   signal diode)
8 Ω speaker

Audio Transformer (Step down)
AC Power Supply or 12.6 VAC Power Transformer

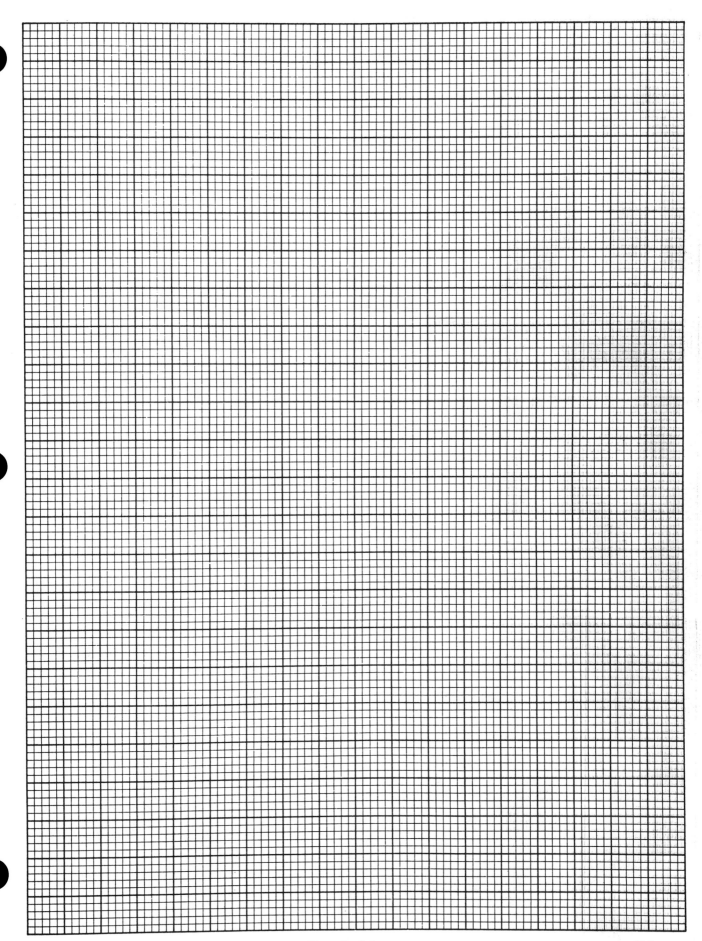

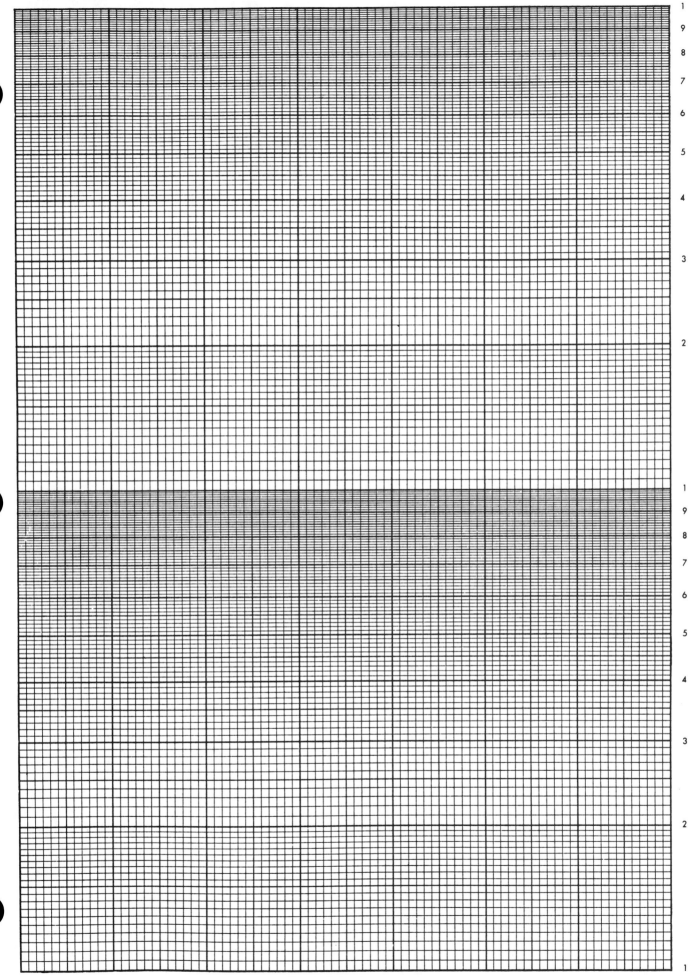

Two-Cycle Semilog Paper

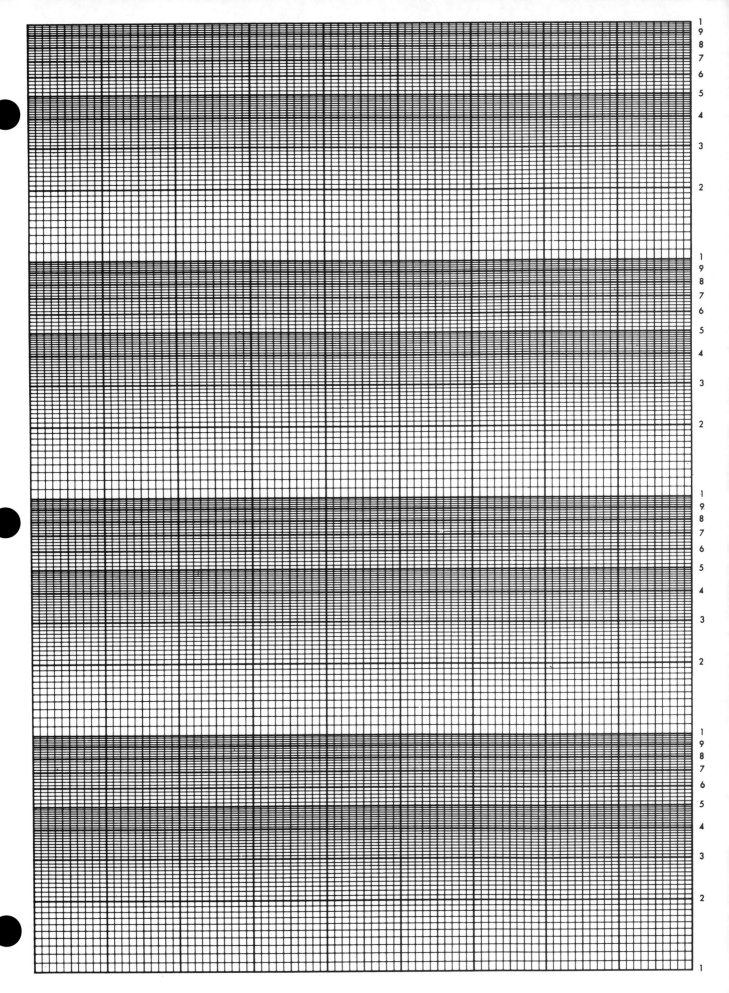